The Lemon Sole

The Lemon Sole

Bennet B. Rae,

M.A., B.Sc., Ph.D., F.R.S.E.

Assistant Director
Dept. of Agriculture and Fisheries for Scotland
Marine Laboratory
Aberdeen

Fishing News (Books) Ltd
110 Fleet St London EC4

A PIONEER
OF FISHERY RESEARCH

Frank Buckland 1826–1880

**This is a Buckland Foundation Book—
one of a series providing a permanent
record of annual lectures maintained
by a bequest of the late Frank Buckland.**

Printed in Great Britain by The Whitefriars Press Ltd.
London and Tonbridge
First Published July, 1965

CONTENTS

LIST OF ILLUSTRATIONS

PREFACE

Francis Trevelyan Buckland, the son of an eminent English clergyman, trained as a surgeon, and on completing his course entered the Army. His interests, however, were mainly in natural history, and before long he gave up his commission and took up studies of the acclimatization of fish, fish hatching and other matters relating to fresh-water fish and fisheries. He started a periodical "Land and Water" in 1866 and wrote numerous articles on the rearing of fresh-water fishes. He was appointed an Inspector of Fisheries in 1867 and, thereafter, devoted nearly all his time to fishery problems. He died in 1880 at the age of fifty-four from an illness brought on by his exertions to supply the Government of New Zealand with salmon eggs at short notice in mid-winter.

Shortly before his death Frank Buckland turned his attention more to the sea, and collaborated with Spencer Walpole in the preparation of a "Report on the Sea Fisheries of England and Wales" which was published in 1879. Appendix I to this report reveals the thorough manner in which these two men gathered information by interviewing fishermen round the entire coastline. In this, and in Appendix II, in which he gives a short history of the commercially important food-fishes, Buckland demonstrates his intensely practical approach to his subject, and follows this up, in Appendix III, with "Observations on Certain Points Connected with the Economy of the Sea Fisheries of England and Wales".

Already at this early date Buckland deplored the catching of undersized fish when he wrote "In order to prevent if possible this terrible destruction it is obvious that we must somehow invent a net which could catch the big fish and let the little ones go". In this sentence and again when he refers to "the great fish farm of the North Sea" Buckland reveals a remarkable foresight, which, in the words of Mr. R. S. Wimpenny, Buckland Professor for 1949, "might at first be set down to a sort of mystical prevision". Such opinions expressed in the face of the generally accepted view of those years, namely that all the sea fisheries were inexhaustible, reveals a remarkable appreciation of the future trend in the fisheries. It is interesting to reflect that well over fifty years were to pass before the United Kingdom first brought regulations into force to conserve fish stocks, by setting limits to the size of the mesh to be used in nets and to the marketable size of fish, and only now, after eighty-five years, are scientists beginning to give serious consideration to the possibility of farming the sea.

Under his will Frank Buckland left to the nation a sum of money with which to endow a Professorship of Economic Fish Culture. The Buckland Foundation, formed in 1926, administers the income derived from the Trust Fund. This provides for the appointment every year of a lecturer to be known as the Buckland Professor, whose duty it is to deliver lectures at such places in the United Kingdom and Ireland as the Trustees may determine. The first Buckland Lectures were given by the late Prof. W. Garstang at Hull and Grimsby in 1930.

In 1958 I was honoured by being appointed Buckland Professor, the subject chosen being "The Lemon Sole". Lectures were given in the first quarter of 1959 at four of the smaller Scottish ports—Wick, Macduff, Arbroath and Whitehills. On the whole the lectures were well attended and interesting discussions were stimulated. Fishermen formed about 80% of the audiences. The lectures dealt with various aspects of the biology and life history of the lemon sole and with different features of the fisheries. In each lecture the importance of the lemon sole in the fisheries economy was stressed, both from a national and a local viewpoint.

I wish to record my appreciation of the help and encouragement given by the late Dr. Alexander Bowman, Scientific Superintendent of the Marine Laboratory of the Fishery Board for Scotland at Aberdeen from 1923 to 1934 and by Mr. James M. Lamont, a member of the staff, in my introduction to research on the lemon sole in 1931. I also wish to thank Dr. C. E. Lucas, the present Director of the Laboratory, now under the Department of Agriculture and Fisheries for Scotland, for his invaluable advice in the preparation of my later papers on this fish. Lastly I wish gratefully to acknowledge the assistance of Mr. J. D. Milne in the preparation of the illustrations to this book.   B. B. R.

Chapter I

IDENTIFICATION AND DISTRIBUTION

POPULAR NAMES

The lemon sole in the past has been known by various names in different parts of the British Isles. Francis Day refers to some of these names in his "Fishes of Great Britain and Ireland", while others appear in a comprehensive list of local names of fishes which has been maintained at the Marine Laboratory, Aberdeen since the beginning of the present century. In some parts of Scotland the fish was known as the Mary-sole, merry-sole, or sand-sole. The name Mary-sole, according to Day, was also applied to the fish in Devonshire and Cornwall, where an alternative name "kit" was also employed. In the Firth of Forth the lemon sole was known as the sand-fluke or smear-dab, the latter being particularly appropriate because of the slime on the fish's skin. Other names include lemon-dab (Belfast), town-dab (Hastings), French-sole (Youghal), sole-fluke (Moray Firth), smooth-dab and bastard-sole. The strangest of all, however, is the name tobacco-fluke, which is understood to have been in use at one time in Aberdeen and on the Kincardineshire coast. The origin of this name is obscure but it may have arisen from the similarity of the colours of the lemon sole to those of certain brands of tobacco.

Since the end of the nineteenth century most of these popular names have disappeared from every-day use, and the name lemon sole or lemon, as it is called by many fishermen, has been adopted throughout the United Kingdom. This development is possibly one inevitable result of the decline of the local fisheries at numerous small ports and the growth of major national fisheries concentrated at a few of the larger ports. The expansion of markets in inland industrial towns and cities, following the development of trawling and the improvement in transport facilities, made it essential to have standard names for the various species of fish being marketed.

The origin of the name lemon sole has often given rise to

speculation but there seems to be little doubt that it represents a corrupt form of a French name for the same fish "limande sole".

SCIENTIFIC NAMES

Despite its popular name the lemon sole is not a member of the Soleidae or sole family. The scientific name by which it was known for many years, *Pleuronectes microcephalus* (Donovan), reveals its affinities with the plaice family or Pleuronectidae, although it has since been reclassified as *Microstomus kitt* (Walbaum) by Norman (1934). Synonyms employed at different times also include various combinations of these names and others—for example *Pleuronectes kitt*, *Pleuronectes microstomus*, *Microstomus microcephalus*, etc. Although the name lemon sole is used to denote species of fish in North America and in New Zealand, these do not refer to *Microstomus kitt* which is confined to the North-East Atlantic.

GENERAL APPEARANCE

The lemon sole is a popular species on the British market. Its small-to-medium size, its oval shape, its smooth, somewhat slimy skin and its characteristically small head and mouth are features which require no detailed description. Although the individual colours of the lemon sole are generally rather dull, the variety of shades of brown and fawn with occasional dashes of mahogany, orange, yellow and green, frequently combine with the speckled or marbled pattern to produce a most pleasing effect. In spite of the absence of bright colours in its make-up this flatfish undoubtedly is one of the most beautiful of our native fishes (see Plate I).

The lemon sole appears to thrive in aquaria where its lively behaviour forms an interesting subject for study.

DISTRIBUTION

Lemon soles are found on the coastal banks of Western Europe from the White Sea to the Bay of Biscay, and, to the north-west, on Rockall and Faroe Banks, round the Faroe Islands and on all coasts of Iceland. The species is not, however, evenly distributed over this extensive area. According to the fishery statistics published by the International Council for the Exploration of

PLATE I. Lemon Sole.

PLATE II. Scale from Lemon Sole of 61 cm—age 21 years.

[*facing page* 12

(1)

(2)

PLATE III. Scales from Tagged Lemon Sole: (1) taken at liberation, 13th July 1922; (2) taken at recapture, 1st August 1924.

TABLE I

Annual European Catches of Lemon Soles 1951–1960 in metric tons and Percentages from the Principal Fishing Grounds

Year	Total Catch	North Sea	W. Scotland	Faroe	Iceland	E. Channel	Irish Sea and Bristol Channel	S. Ireland	W. Ireland	Bay of Biscay
1951	9388	50·2	2·3	13·4	21·5	3·3	1·4	2·4	0·2	2·4
1952	9433	52·2	2·7	11·9	18·0	3·2	1·3	2·8	0·1	5·1
1953	9786	55·6	3·7	8·4	16·6	3·9	2·4	2·7	0·2	5·1
1954	8822	45·0	3·7	10·7	18·2	6·1	1·5	5·1	0·5	7·8
1955	8934	44·7	3·6	8·8	14·9	5·9	1·7	10·0	0·2	7·7
1956	8260	42·8	5·0	9·0	18·0	4·5	2·3	7·8	1·0	8·5
1957	10,750	33·2	3·9	9·5	24·0	4·2	3·6	11·4	2·8	6·6
1958	9550	34·3	4·2	10·1	16·9	4·8	2·5	14·3	4·0	7·8
1959	10,239	37·0	3·2	10·8	15·9	4·1	2·0	16·0	4·1	5·6
1960	12,018	34·9	3·7	11·5	18·4	2·0	7·1	14·9	1·1	3·8

the Sea in the *Bulletin Statistique,* the yearly landings of lemon
soles, in the ten years, 1951–1960, ranged from 8,260 to 12,018
metric tons. The percentages of the yearly catches from the
principal fishing grounds where the species is caught are given
in Table I.

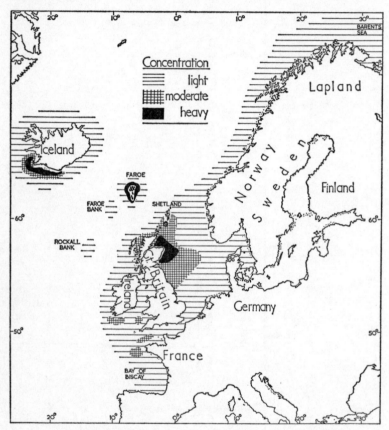

FIG. 1. Distribution and main concentrations of Lemon Soles.

This shows that the North Sea is by far the most important
region for lemon soles, providing from 33 to 56% of the total
catch. Although its share of the catch has fallen from 1951 to
1960, the annual yield from this region has not declined to any
appreciable extent, so that the apparent decline in the North
Sea percentage is due rather to an increase in the landings

from other regions. Over the ten years, Iceland has provided the second highest proportion of the catch, from 15 to 24%, and Faroe the third highest, from 8 to 13%. In the second half of the decade, however, landings from the southern regions increased in a remarkable manner, and, in particular, the grounds off the south of Ireland have proved so productive as to displace the Faroes from the third position of importance. Landings from the Barents Sea, the Norwegian coast, the Skagerrak, Kattegat, Belt Sea and Rockall Bank are insignificant and have not been included in Table I.

The general distribution and the main concentrations of the lemon sole in the north-east Atlantic are shown in Figure 1. The concentrations in the north-western North Sea, on the coastal banks of the Faroe Islands and off south and south-west Iceland have long been evident as a result of fishing operations by commercial and research vessels. The exact location of the concentrations giving rise to the recent, improved landings from the southern grounds, however, has not yet been accurately determined. The latter grounds are, therefore, indicated rather tentatively on the chart.

Chapter II

THE LEMON SOLE FISHERIES

As may be expected, the commercial catch of lemon soles is not shared equally by all the fishing nations of Western Europe. Indeed, international statistics reveal that the greater part of the landings, from 75 to 91%, is accounted for by three countries—Scotland, England and France—while the remaining 25 to 9% is shared by Belgium, Denmark, Germany, Holland, Iceland and Sweden. Landings in other countries such as Norway, Poland, Spain and Eire may be assumed to be too small to justify the keeping of separate records of this species.

The Scottish, English and French shares of the lemon sole catch are given in Table II. This shows that from 1951 to 1960 the Scottish and English shares of the fishery have tended to decline slowly, while the French share has increased to nearly four times its 1951 total. Landings in Scotland, however, despite fluctuations arising from various causes, have not declined to any appreciable extent in the ten-year period and English landings, although considerably less than they were in the period between the two wars, have been reasonably maintained from 1951 to 1960. The decline in the Scottish and English shares is, therefore, more apparent than real—the result, it would seem, of the increase in the landings as a whole. Further reference to international fishery statistics in the *Bulletin Statistique* reveals that the increase in the French catch has come largely from the English Channel, the Irish Sea and Bristol Channel, the south of Ireland and the Bay of Biscay. It seems unlikely that these southern grounds have suddenly become more productive in lemon soles, so that one must conclude that the heavier landings of this species by French fishermen have followed an increase in the fishing effort and possibly the adoption of more effective methods or gears.

TABLE II

Landings of Lemon Soles in metric tons by all European Countries (T)
with Quantities Landed in Scotland (S), England and Wales (E)
and France (F) and each expressed as Percentages of the Total.

	T	S	E	F
1951	9388	3540	2824	723
		37·7	30·1	7·7 = 75·5
1952	9433	3634	3256	1035
		38·5	34·5	11·0 = 84·0
1953	9786	3647	3956	1128
		37·3	40·4	11·5 = 89·2
1954	8822	3281	2997	1639
		37·2	34·0	18·6 = 89·8
1955	8934	3242	2743	2141
		36·3	30·7	24·0 = 91·0
1956	8260	3178	2239	1762
		38·5	27·1	21·3 = 86·9
1957	10,750	3252	2666	2763
		30·3	24·8	25·7 = 80·8
1958	9550	3058	2595	2932
		32·0	27·2	30·7 = 89·9
1959	10,239	3390	2788	2997
		33·0	27·2	29·3 = 89·5
1960	12,018	3455	3065	3435
		28·6	25·5	28·6 = 82·7

THE SCOTTISH FISHERY
From 1882 to the First Great War

It is evident from Table II that the major part of the lemon sole
catch is taken by British fishermen. It is, therefore, relevant to
study the Scottish and English fisheries in greater detail. For

this purpose the annual reports and statistical tables for
Scottish fisheries have been utilized. The systematic collection
of fishery statistics in the United Kingdom was begun in 1809
by the Commissioners of the British White Herring Fishery.
These records, which represent the quantities of herring cured
in Scotland and include quantities of salted cod, ling and hake,
were maintained until the appointment of the Fishery Board
for Scotland in 1882. The first annual report by the Board was
issued for the year 1882. In this year the first Aberdeen steam
trawler—a second-hand, wooden paddle-boat, of 28 tons and
50 h.p., commenced fishing off the port, although a few small
sail-powered trawlers had been operating in Scottish waters
for some years before this. In the second annual report more
detailed statistics were published about the species and quantities of the fish landed and for the first time lemon soles were
distinguished from other species of flatfish. Landings of lemon
soles in Scotland from 1883 to 1962 have been extracted and
summarised in Table III. This gives—

(1) the landings for 1883 and 1884 and, thereafter, the
    average landings for each five-yearly period up to the
    present time;

(2) the proportions of the catch taken by trawl and by other
    methods;

(3) the annual or average annual value of the lemon sole
    catch;

(4) the average price per cwt paid to the fishermen.

Throughout the nineteenth century the traditional Scottish
fisheries were the drift-net fisheries for herring which were
prosecuted seasonally from different parts of the coast. Fishing
for white or demersal fish, those species living on or near the
sea bottom, was of secondary importance. Most of the white
fish caught at that time were taken by baited hooks and lines—
plaice, dabs, haddock and whiting by small lines, and cod,
ling, saithe, skate and halibut by great lines. Some of these
species, particularly cod, were also caught by means of set or
anchored nets. Small quantities of other species were also
taken by these methods, including anything up to a few
hundred cwt of lemon soles.

The Lemon Sole Fisheries 19

TABLE III

Average Annual Landings in cwt of Lemon Soles by British Vessels in Scotland from 1883 to 1962, the Proportions by Trawl and by other Methods, the Average Annual Value and the Average Value per cwt.

Period	Annual or Average Annual Catch cwt	% by Trawl	% by Other Methods	Annual or Average Annual Value £	Average Price per cwt s. d.
1883	1702	—	—	3225	37 11
1884	4163	—	—	5589	26 10
1885–1889	10,454	97·7	2·3	13,736	26 3
1890–1894	18,578	98·7	1·3	30,836	33 2
1895–1899	18,389	99·0	1·0	38,231	41 7
1900–1904	24,320	99·3	0·7	48,641	40 0
1905–1909	34,423	99·1	0·9	66,917	38 11
1910–1914	39,866	99·0	1·0	82,742	41 6
1915–1919	16,532	97·6	2·4	76,449	92 6
1920–1924	38,598	86·2	13·8	162,866	84 5
1925–1929	55,636	82·7	17·3	234,672	84 4
1930–1934	61,928	79·8	20·2	240,722	77 9
1935–1939	66,256	75·5	24·5	249,094	75 2
1940–1944	33,431	61·4	38·5	204,248	122 2
1945–1949	40,943	74·6	25·4	214,621	104 10
1950–1954	62,389	64·6	35·4	436,833	140 0
1955–1959	56,406	53·7	46·3	479,607	170 1
1960–1962	64,402	51·1	48·9	554,031	172 1

The introduction of steam trawling to Aberdeen (Scotland's leading fishing port) in 1882 immediately resulted in a rapid increase in the quantities of lemon soles landed annually over the next eight years. This increase may be attributed to the new method of fishing and not to any sudden increase in the stocks of lemon soles available. Up to 1882 it seems clear that the methods employed to catch white fish were not suitable for the capture of lemon soles and certain other species. Although small quantities of lemon soles had been taken and continued to be taken by baited hooks on small lines, the technique employed in line fishing and the nature of the bait used would appear to

B 2

have been designed primarily to catch the commoner fish such as haddock, plaice and codling. It seems probable, too, that small-line fishing was prosecuted mainly on grounds favourable to these species but not so favourable to lemon soles.

Despite the rapid expansion of the trawling industry in the last decade of the nineteenth century (the number of trawlers based in Aberdeen rose from 38 in 1892 to 156 in 1902), the annual catch of lemon soles remained relatively stable at just over 18,000 cwt from 1890 to 1898. In 1899, however, landings again took an upward trend, which continued without interruption almost to the outbreak of the first World War, by which time the number of trawlers at Aberdeen had increased to 249.

In almost any fishery the most abundant species of fish on the fishing grounds generally provide the bulk of the catch and naturally these fish form the main objective of the fishermen. Consequently, in the early days of trawling, the predominant species such as cod, haddock, whiting and plaice were the principal types caught and landed in Scotland. The capture of the relatively little known lemon sole was, therefore, incidental to the other fisheries, at least up to the first World War.

The second period of increase in the lemon sole landings from 1899 to 1912 would, therefore, appear to be the result, to some extent, of the expansion of the trawl fishery. At the same time, the effect on the catch of the replacement of the original trawl, the beam trawl, by the newly-evolved otter trawl, cannot be disregarded. This new trawl, first designed by a Mr. Scott of Granton in 1894, was an immediate success, and by the end of the century was in general use on Scottish steam trawlers. Although its success was mainly measured by the larger catches of roundfish (i.e. cod, haddock and whiting), its greater efficiency in waters deeper than those normally fished by the beam trawl may well have contributed to the improved landings of lemon soles. This possibility seems all the stronger when one considers that the average depth at which lemon soles are caught is somewhat greater than that at which plaice, the commonest flatfish of commercial importance in Scottish waters, are taken.

From the outbreak of war in 1914 trawlers and their crews began to be withdrawn gradually for other duties. The reduction in fishing activity naturally resulted in lower landings of all kinds of fish, and the average annual catch of lemon soles in these years declined to a lower total than at any time since 1890.

Columns 3 and 4 of Table III show the method by which lemon soles were taken. Up to the end of the first Great War the bulk of the catch, over 97%, was taken by trawlers, while the small remainder was obtained by various means, including small lines, set nets and flounder seines.

The Inter-war Period

With the return of trawlers and their crews from war service fishing was resumed as quickly as the fishing grounds could be cleared of mines, and heavy landings of all kinds of fish resulted from the exploitation of the stocks which had accumulated during the relaxation of fishing. Lemon sole landings soon attained their pre-war level, and thereafter continued to in-increase until the late 1930s, by which time they had more than quadrupled their wartime average. This extraordinary development is all the more surprising when one considers that from 1935 to 1939 stocks of the commoner species of fish in the North Sea were showing unmistakable signs of over-fishing.

The remarkable increase in the quantities of lemon soles caught annually after the first war appear to have resulted from a number of causes. In the first place the number of trawlers continued to increase (the Aberdeen total amounted to 285 in 1934), although this increase was to some extent offset by the declining efficiency of many units of the fishing fleet, 60% of which was over 20 years of age. At the same time, however, the fishing efficiency of many vessels was augmented by the adoption of new methods and gear, particularly by the introduction of a French improvement on the otter trawl known as the "Vigneron Dahl" gear. Moreover, trawling was made possible on rougher grounds by the use of "bobbins" on the groundrope—a device which helps to ease the net and cod-end over obstacles on the sea bottom. The latter innovation may have increased the lemon sole catch considerably since this species is known sometimes to frequent rough grounds.

Nevertheless, the main increase in the lemon sole catch probably resulted from quite a different cause, namely the introduction of the Danish seine-net and the development of the Scottish seine-net fishery. This gear was brought to Scot-

land in the years following the first Great War at a time when
considerable hardship was being experienced by Scottish
fishermen as a result of the failure of the great herring fishery.
The operation of the seine-net was quickly mastered by Moray
Firth fishermen, and gradually, its use was extended to all
Scottish coasts. From the introduction of the Danish seine in
1921 to the outbreak of the second Great War the catch by
Scottish seiners rose steadily and with it the catch of lemon soles,
except in certain years when herring fishery prospects appeared
more promising, thus temporarily attracting some of the
fishermen back to drifting for herring. In 1939, seiners caught
nearly 18,000 cwt of lemon soles, rather less than half of the
quantity taken by trawlers. This important addition to the
lemon sole fishery is clearly indicated in column 4 of Table III.
From 2·4% taken by various means during the first war, the
percentage rose to 24·5% prior to the second war, an increase
which was almost entirely due to seining since the quantities
taken by small-lines, etc., fell to negligible amounts after 1919.

From the Outbreak of the Second Great War to 1962

During the second Great War fishing vessels were again
required for other duties and landings of all kinds of fish
declined sharply. It is interesting to note, however, that the
annual landings of lemon soles remained relatively high and that
the average for the years 1940 to 1944 during the second Great
War was twice the average for the 1915 to 1919 period, and
indeed might have been greater if all lemon soles had been
recorded as such during the second war. There are several
reasons for this unusual feature of the 1940 to 1944 landings.
In the first place, the seine-net fleet, which was not in existence
during the first war, continued to operate in the Moray Firth
where, unlike many other grounds, fishing was permitted
throughout the second war. Furthermore, the ban on trawling
by British vessels within the Moray Firth, which had been in
force since 1895, was lifted temporarily for the outer half of the
Firth. Thus both seiners and some of the few remaining
trawlers were allowed to fish the rich lemon sole grounds of the
Moray Firth.

Landings of lemon soles were also maintained during the
second war by a small fleet of trawlers continuing to fish the

Faroese grounds, though somewhat intermittently, from 1939 to 1945. Like the Moray Firth the Faroese grounds are also a rich source of lemon soles.

The part played by seiners in maintaining the lemon sole landings during the second war is perhaps best illustrated by the proportion of the total catch, 38·5%, procured by this method (see Table III).

During the second war stocks of all kinds of fish accumulated on North Sea and other grounds following the five to six years' respite from heavy fishing activity, just as they did during the first war. Consequently, at the close of hostilities in 1945, fishermen once more were able to reap a rich harvest. On this occasion, because of the scarcity of food in Europe, the system of controls, instituted during the war to keep prices steady and to encourage bulk landings of fish, was continued after the end of the war until 1950. This helped to increase landings of fish generally, but owing to the control prices for plaice and lemon soles being the same, these two species were frequently not separated on the market, so that quantities of lemon soles were often recorded under plaice, the commoner of the two species within the North Sea. Accordingly, the records of the annual landings of lemon soles from 1941 to 1950 are certainly lower than they would have been if no controls had been in operation.

In the immediate post-war period, 1945–49, landings of lemon soles nevertheless increased, mainly it would seem from trawling, since this method accounted for three-quarters of the catch, and the share by seining fell to a quarter of the total. But from 1950 onwards several changes became evident in the lemon sole fishery. Although a number of new trawlers were added to the Scottish trawler fleet after the war, the average condition of the vessels in the fleet had deteriorated as the result of age and of war service, and further difficulties were experienced in regard to the rising costs of maintenance and replacement. In consequence the state of the fleet as a whole declined, both in numbers and in the general efficiency of the individual units. This deterioration continued until the early 1950s when, with government assistance, a start was at last made with the replacement of the trawler fleet (consisting predominantly of coal-fired steamers) by modern vessels, many of them diesel-powered. Although the new vessels were much more costly to build than the old trawlers had been, they proved to be more efficient and economical to run. This meant that fewer trawlers were required to supply the market, and the result of this combination of factors was that by 1962 the number of Aberdeen trawlers had fallen to 137 vessels, representing about 83% of the total Scottish trawler fleet.

The Expansion of the Seine-net Fishery

While this change in the composition of the trawler fleet was taking place, a change was also taking place in the seine-net fleet. This method of fishing, which had been developing steadily between the two wars and was based principally on the medium-sized and smaller ports, entered a period of rapid expansion at the end of the second war. Almost entirely motor or diesel-powered, this section of the fishing fleet held a number of advantages over the steam-powered and coal-fired trawlers. The smaller size of the seiners, their lower initial costs and their more economic running costs all operated in their favour. From the end of the war, later with government assistance, the numbers of seiners began to rise and with this rise came an increase in the average size and power of the individual vessels.

Seine-net fishermen have frequently demonstrated their ability to improve on existing gear and methods. Even between the wars the original technique employed in working the Danish seine-net was largely abandoned, and a new technique, known as "fly-dragging", was evolved by Scottish fishermen. This method proved particularly successful in fishing for roundfish, which form the bulk of the Scottish white-fish catch, and undoubtedly was one of the important factors in the post-war development of the seine-net fishery (Ritchie, 1960). Among other things this expansion of the fishery was characterized by a gradual extension of the areas worked by seiners to deeper, off-shore grounds, sometimes at a considerable distance from their base port. Inevitably this has led to the partial exclusion of trawlers from grounds hitherto regarded as trawling preserves.

Although the rise in the seine-net catch has consisted predominantly of haddock, whiting and codling, the quantities of flatfish, notably plaice and lemon soles, have also increased. From a yearly average of just over 10,000 cwt for the period 1945 to 1949, representing 25% of the total landings by all methods, landings of lemon soles from seine-netting have risen to an average of over 31,000 cwt for the three years 1960 to 1962, or 48·9% of the total landings by all methods.

When one considers that the lemon sole catches from Iceland and Faroe are obtained entirely by trawl, it is clear that the proportion of the landings by seiners from home waters must be well over 50%. An examination of the quantities landed each year from the North Sea shows that, excluding the period from 1940 to 1946 when few trawlers were operating, landings of lemon soles by seine-netters have consistently exceeded the landings by trawlers since 1956. Moreover, the proportion taken by seine-net in the North Sea is increasing steadily, with the result that, in the years 1960 to 1962, 68% of the lemon soles was caught by seine-net and only 32% by trawl. On the less important west of Scotland grounds the proportion by seine is even greater, almost 75%, so that in Scottish waters generally it may be concluded that the seine-net is supplanting the trawl as the principal means of catching lemon soles.

Proportions of Scottish Catch from the Various Fishing Grounds

In 1922 the Fishery Board for Scotland began to publish the quantities of each species of fish from the different grounds fished by Scottish fishermen. The quantities and percentages of lemon soles landed in Scotland are summarized in Table IV. This shows that the North Sea is the main source of this fish, as, indeed, it has been since the start of trawling in 1882, and that Faroe comes second in importance, but a long way behind. Over the last forty years the quantity from the North Sea has fluctuated, but considering the possible effects of natural fluctuations, changes in fishing intensity, and the influence of the second war, the annual yield has remained remarkably high and shows little evidence of a decline. Nevertheless, it will be noted that the proportion of the catch from the North Sea has tended to fall, although this obviously is owing to bigger landings from other grounds, such as Faroe and the west of Scotland.

TABLE IV

Proportions from the Various Grounds of Scottish Catch of Lemon Soles 1922–1962

Years	Average Annual Catch cwt	N. Sea	Average Catch from			Various
			W. Scotland	Faroe	Iceland	
1922–1924	39521	31559 80%	2327 6%	4028 10%	555 1%	1051 3%
1925–1929	55636	46137 83%	3580 6%	4283 8%	325 +	1311 2%
1930–1934	61928	47326 76%	2993 5%	9604 16%	608 1%	1396 2%
1935–1939	66256	54165 82%	1588 2%	7757 12%	1484 2%	1262 2%
1940–1944	33431	19458 58%	2163 7%	9849 30%	1462 4%	499 1%
1945–1949	40943	22021 54%	964 2%	14552 36%	1380 3%	2023 5%
1950–1954	62389	45071 72%	2816 5%	13353 21%	897 1%	252 +
1955–1959	56406	39915 71%	5243 9%	10939 19%	306 +	2 +
1960–1962	64402	40840 63%	4670 7%	17174 27%	1690 3%	29 +

Scottish landings from Faroe, despite fluctuations arising from various causes, have risen appreciably over the last forty years. At first, up to the early 1930s, this increase was undoubtedly the result of a growing fishing effort by Scottish trawlers. In the late 1930s Scottish lemon sole landings from Faroe declined, but during the war they recovered and reached a higher yearly average than in any previous period, in spite of the smaller fishing effort. In the immediate post-war period even greater quantities of lemon soles were caught, mainly it would seem from the war-time accumulation of the stock. A decline then set in over the next ten years, to be followed by a remarkable recovery in the three years 1960–62, when Scottish landings of lemon soles from Faroe reached a record average of over 17,000 cwt. This increase, which is all the more surprising since trawlers were excluded from some of the rich lemon sole grounds by the decision of the Faroese to extend their fishing limits in 1959, appears to have been attained, to some extent at least, by an increase in the Scottish fishing effort. It is difficult, however, to suggest a satisfactory explanation of the increase since the situation at Faroe has been complicated by a number of factors. In the first place the main Scottish trawling effort on these grounds is for haddock and cod; secondly, the extension of fishing limits has forced trawlers to operate on the whole in deeper water sometimes outside the well-known lemon sole grounds; and thirdly, because the natural fluctuations in the lemon sole stock are imperfectly known for this period.

Unlike the landings from the North Sea and from Faroe, those from Iceland are small and have never exceeded 4% of the annual average in any period of years.

These quantities of lemon soles from the various grounds demonstrate the emphasis of the Scottish fishing effort as a whole on home waters and to a less degree on middle distance grounds such as those at Faroe.

The Importance of the Lemon Sole in Scottish Fisheries

The haddock is by far the most important demersal fish in Scottish fisheries. From 1958 to 1962 British vessels annually landed from one to one-and-a-half million cwt of haddock at Scottish ports, representing on an average 34% of the total annual catch of demersal fish by all methods. The combined catches of the three gadoids, haddock, cod and whiting, amounted to 76% of the total catch of all species in the same period. The relative importance of the principal demersal food

fishes by weight landed is illustrated in Figure 2. In contrast to
the annual yield of the three abundant gadoid species, the
quantities of each of the other species landed were almost insignificant. Landings of the three most plentiful flatfishes,
plaice, lemon sole and halibut, together amounted to less than

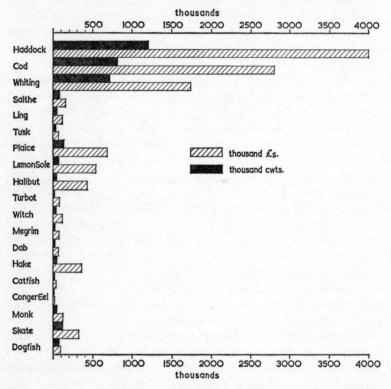

FIG. 2. Average yearly landings and values of the demersal food fishes by British
vessels in Scotland, 1958–62.

6% of the average annual total and of this lemon soles accounted for only 1·7%.

The success of a fishery, however, does not depend entirely
on the yield. The demand for fish on the market is a factor of
particular importance which influences the price and consequently the profitability or otherwise of the fishing operations.
Some species in the course of time have acquired considerable

popularity with the consumer, thus creating a keen demand for them on the market. This has resulted in a grading of prices which tends to be maintained from year to year unless, as sometimes happens, plentiful supplies or scarcity of a particular species causes a reduction or an increase in prices. The prices paid to the fishermen, therefore, reflect the interaction of supply and demand.

The total value of each of the principal species sold on Scottish markets is also given in Figure 2. Haddock, cod and whiting (76% of the total landings) together account for 72% of the total value of all demersal species, while the much less abundant plaice, lemon sole and halibut (5·9% of the total landings) account for 14% of the total value. Of the latter percentage lemon soles bring in 4·5%.

It is obvious, therefore, that the lemon sole, like some other flatfishes, is of much greater importance to Scottish fishermen than the relatively modest quantities caught would indicate. At the present time it ranks second in order of importance to halibut in average price per cwt (see Figure 3) so that a catch which includes a high proportion of lemon soles may be expected to be particularly remunerative, and even a few boxes of this fish may ensure a profitable trip, especially in times of scarcity when prices may soar to as high as £24 a cwt, i.e., nearly three times the average price.

It is interesting to study the increase in the average annual value of the lemon sole from its first appearance as a separate species in the Scottish fishery statistics in 1883 (see Table III, column 5). From a modest total of just over £3000 in that year the revenue to Scottish fishermen from this species has increased to well over £500,000 in each year since 1959, and in 1962 it even approached £600,000. In the last column of Table III the average price per cwt in the various periods reflects phases in the fishery. Although at times prices have tended to fall, for example, from 1883 to 1889 and again in the period between the two wars, doubtless with the growing production of lemon soles, the trend generally has been upwards with two marked increases during the inflationary periods of the two wars. This fish, therefore, makes an important contribution to the economics of the Scottish fishing industry and particularly to the section concentrating on the exploitation of home waters.

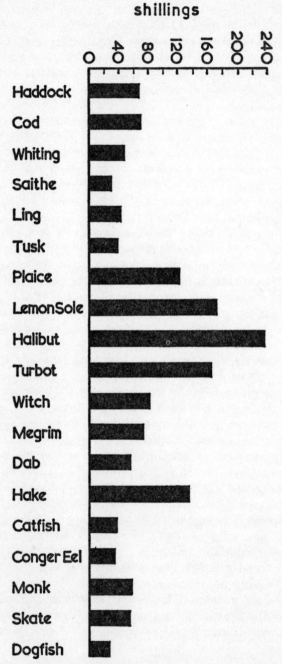

FIG. 3. Average price per cwt of demersal fish landings in Scotland, 1958–62.

THE ENGLISH AND WELSH FISHERIES

Although the published fishery statistics for England and Wales are not so detailed as the Scottish tables for the last twenty years of the nineteenth century, it seems certain that quantities of lemon soles were being landed in England and Wales by sailing beam trawlers before 1882 when the Scottish lemon sole fishery may be said to have started. Moreover, there seems no reason to doubt that greater quantities of lemon soles were landed in England and Wales than in Scotland every year up to the first war. After the war landings of lemon soles increased rapidly in both countries to reach their peaks of over 100,000 cwt in England and over 70,000 in Scotland in 1935. During the second war and up to 1950, annual landings of this species in England and Wales were the lowest on record in the present century, but these undoubtedly reflect the effect of the system of price controls in force at this time, and cannot be regarded as representing the true quantities of lemon soles caught in these years. Indeed the English records from 1941 to 1949 appear to be even less reliable than the Scottish records, probably because the lemon sole in England is relatively less abundant and less important than the plaice, with the result that lemon soles during the period of the controls tended to be marketed as plaice or other species more frequently than in Scotland.

Following the abolition of the wartime regulations in 1950 landings of lemon soles in England and Wales again increased, but only to the extent of a little over half of their quantity in the peak period of the 1930s. Some explanation of the failure of the English landings of this fish to regain their former abundance may be obtained later from a breakdown of the average yearly catches according to their place of origin.

Up to the first war lemon soles landed in England and Wales were, as in Scotland, taken almost entirely by trawl. Between the wars trawlers continued to provide 98% or more of the English catch, and, unlike the situation in Scotland, there was no development of a seine-net fishery. After the second war the proportion of the catch by nets other than trawl began to rise, slowly at first and then more rapidly as the following percentages show:—

Period	Average annual catch in cwt	Percentage by trawl	Percentage by other methods, mainly seine
1945–1949	12,138	97·0	3·0
1950–1954	54,783	93·9	6·1
1955–1959	45,595	92·8	7·2
1960–1962	52,413	80·8	19·2

This change is clearly the result of an increase in seining from English ports, as the numbers of voyages by English-based seiners in the North Sea increased from less than 2000 in 1950 to over 6000 in each year since 1957. Furthermore, the quantity of lemon soles taken by seine-net in the North Sea increased from just over 3000 cwt in 1958 to over 12,000 in 1962. In the latter year, too, landings of lemon soles by seiners from the North Sea exceeded the landings by trawlers from the same area for the first time. Although the number of English seine-net vessels has certainly increased, a considerable share of the seine-net landings in recent years has undoubtedly been provided by Scottish vessels temporarily, and seasonally, based on English ports.

The high proportion of trawled lemon soles in English landings is, therefore, accounted for partly by the preponderance of trawlers in the fishing fleets and partly by the modest and comparatively late development of the seine-net fishery in England and Wales. There is, however, another reason which becomes apparent from a study of Table V showing the various grounds from which the English catch has been procured over the years. This reveals that a high proportion of the English catch since the war has originated from Iceland and Faroe, where trawling is practically the only method of fishing engaged in by English fishermen.

Proportions of the English and Welsh Catch from the Various Fishing Grounds

Table V shows that prior to the first war more than half of the English catch of lemon soles came from the North Sea, with

Quantities and Percentages of the English and Welsh Catch of Lemon Soles from the Different Fishing Grounds

Average Annual Catch in cwt

Years	All areas	N. Sea	W. Scotland incl. Rockall	Iceland	Faroe	Irish Sea	S. & W. Ireland	Bristol C.	English C.	Norwegian C. Barents Sea
1906–1909	49015	28734	1476	4926	7746	390	1451	1795	1656	—
		58·6	3·0	10·1	15·8	0·8	2·9	3·7	3·4	—
1910–1914	54437	27558	1242	6798	12037	463	1247	1858	2100	6
		50·6	2·3	12·5	22·1	0·9	2·3	3·4	3·9	+
1915–1919	18686	—	—	—	—	—	—	—	—	—
1920–1924	37711	13495	2419	8174	8967	696	1149	882	1375	67
		35·8	6·4	21·7	23·8	1·8	3·0	2·3	3·6	0·1
1925–1929	66846	21862	2292	20790	13534	1144	2127	1631	2889	81
		32·7	3·4	31·1	20·2	1·7	3·2	2·4	4·3	0·1
1930–1934	96098	23551	4349	33875	22043	2699	3300	3648	1999	258
		24·5	4·5	35·3	22·9	2·8	3·4	3·8	2·1	0·3
1935–1938	94272	21955	5043	43354	15033	1503	3227	2185	1677	239
		23·3	5·3	45·9	15·9	1·6	3·4	2·3	1·8	0·3
1939–1945	22239	—	—	—	—	—	—	—	—	—
1946–1949	13608	1198	256	5431	6148	36	28	42	421	49
		8·8	1·8	40·0	45·2	0·3	0·2	0·3	3·1	0·3
1950–1954	54783	19852	1642	21523	6341	1011	1552	912	1821	129
		36·2	3·0	39·3	11·6	1·8	2·8	1·7	3·3	0·2
1955–1959	45595	14328	1240	19740	5220	903	1290	1186	1707	91
		31·4	2·7	43·3	11·4	2·0	2·7	2·6	3·7	0·2
1960–1962	52413	22830	1110	20704	4049	475	404	1188	1570	76
		43·6	2·1	39·5	7·7	0·9	0·8	2·3	3·0	0·1

the Faroes second and Iceland third in order of importance. Between the two wars, when English landings as a whole were mounting to their peak in the 1930s, the yield from the North Sea remained fairly stable, while the catch from Iceland rose rapidly to five times its average amount for the five years 1920 to 1924. Landings from Faroe also increased up to 1930 to 1934, but declined in the late 1930s, mainly it would seem through the withdrawal of trawlers from that area. Immediately prior to the second war, nearly half of the lemon soles on the English market were obtained at Iceland while less than one-quarter of the total came from the North Sea. It is interesting to note that landings from the subsidiary grounds such as the west of Scotland, the Irish Sea, south and west of Ireland, the Bristol Channel and the English Channel, also attained their highest yield of lemon soles between the wars.

After the second war further changes are evident from Table V. Disregarding the rather artificial quantities and percentages for the "control" years 1946 to 1949, it will be observed that the Icelandic totals have since declined to about half their maximum of the period 1935 to 1938, and that the formerly heavy, English landings from Faroe have also declined in 1960 to 1962 to less than one-fifth of their record yield from this area in the years 1930 to 1934. The reduction in the catch of lemon soles from each of these areas would appear, to a considerable extent, to be associated with the decisions by the authorities in Iceland and Faroe to extend their fishery limits from three to twelve miles. Despite certain temporary concessions the effect of this action has been to exclude British trawlers from certain rich lemon sole grounds. This has fallen particularly heavily on English trawlers operating on Icelandic grounds, and since there is no comparable area from which lemon soles could be obtained there seems to be little likelihood of any appreciable increase in the supplies of this fish on the English market.

In general, too, the quantities of lemon soles from the subsidiary grounds have also tended to fall off. This is somewhat surprising since, as Table II shows, the French catch of lemon soles from these grounds has increased in the last eight years. It would seem, therefore, that English fishermen have to a considerable extent been displaced from these southern

grounds by the French. In view of the recent expansion of the
seine-net fishery in England and Wales, it will be interesting
to see if this method of fishing succeeds in regaining some of the
lost ground.

The North Sea alone has been providing more lemon soles to
the English market in recent years and this, as has already been
noted, may be attributed to the growth of seining in English
waters.

The Relative Value of the Lemon Sole in English and Welsh Fisheries

The average annual quantity of demersal fish landed by British
vessels in England and Wales over the period 1958 to 1962
amounted to over 10,000,000 cwt and the value to over 35
million pounds sterling. Of these totals cod alone provided
rather more than half of both the catch and the value. The
average lemon sole catch for the same period barely exceeded
50,000 cwt and the value rather more than £400,000. The
latter figures represent 0·5% of the total catch and 1·2% of the
total value of all demersal species. When compared with the
corresponding Scottish proportions of 1·7% and 4·5% respectively, it is evident that the lemon sole is relatively of much
greater importance to Scottish fisheries than to the English.
Nevertheless the lemon sole ranks amongst those species fetch-
ing a high price on the English market. In the last five years it
has commanded an average price of 162s. 10d. per cwt and
has occupied the sixth or seventh place in order of value
after common sole, red mullet, halibut, hake, brill and sometimes turbot. This compares unfavourably with the equivalent
Scottish price of 172s. 11d. per cwt, but may be explained by
the high proportion of Icelandic fish of poorer average quality
than North Sea fish on the English market. Despite its relative
unimportance the lemon sole is still a desirable fish to any
fisherman.

Chapter III

PELAGIC PHASE OF THE LIFE HISTORY

Spawning Places

The wide distribution of the lemon sole in the north-east Atlantic has already been noted (Figure 1). From the occurrence of ripe and spawning fish in the catches of Scottish research vessels it has been concluded that the species may spawn wherever it is found. This conclusion finds support from the occurrence of the eggs and larvae of lemon soles in the plankton. However, it is also apparent from research and commercial records that most of the spawning takes place in certain favoured places within the areas where the fish are normally found in dense concentrations. Thus in the north-western North Sea the heaviest spawning occurs off the Scottish east coast, but west of 1°W longitude, from the latitude of Caithness across the outer Moray Firth to the Banffshire and Aberdeenshire coasts and southwards to Montrose Bank. Smaller concentrations have also been located between Foula and Fair Isle and in the vicinity of the Butt of Lewis and Cape Wrath, and minor concentrations occur locally on the west coast from the Flannan Isles to the Firth of Clyde.

Spawning also takes place on all coastal banks at Faroe and Iceland and on Faroe Bank, but is heaviest at points within the areas where lemon soles are most numerous.

It is evident that a species with such a wide distribution and apparently able to survive under such variable physical features of depth, temperature, etc. as the lemon sole, is not restricted to any particular set of conditions for spawning. Nevertheless in the north-western North Sea spawning is mainly confined to depths of 30 to 50 fathoms, and, following a survey of the occurrence of lemon sole larvae in Scottish plankton collections in 1929, 1930 and 1931, it was concluded that no spawning had taken place in Scottish waters until the water on the sea floor had attained a temperature of 6·5°C. Although there would appear to be certain optimum conditions

36

for the spawning of lemon soles in Scottish waters, and it may be assumed that spawning in other areas is also largely governed by environmental factors, it does not necessarily follow that the conditions in the various areas are always the same.

SPAWNING PERIOD

Early investigations (McIntosh, 1897) indicated that the spawning of the lemon sole extended over at least seven months of the year, from February to August. Later Bowman and Rae (1935) confirmed the long spawning period by a study of the occurrence of ripe and maturing fish. Ripe or nearly ripe males were taken in almost every month of the year in Scottish waters, although no ripe females were recorded before April or later than September. Investigation of the occurrence of the larvae in the three years 1929 to 1931 threw further light on this subject. This showed that spawning of the lemon sole in the Scottish area begins on the west coast at the beginning of April or even, in some years, in the second half of March. It then spreads rapidly northwards to the west of the Hebrides and through the Minch to the north coast and the west coasts of Orkney and Shetland. On the west coast of Scotland spawning would seem to be completed by the end of July, while on the north coast and west of Orkney it may persist to the end of August, and on the west side of Shetland even into September.

It is interesting to note that in each of the three years 1929 to 1931 the first lemon sole larvae caught within the North Sea were taken at the eastern ends of the entrances from the Atlantic in May. Most of these specimens were beyond the youngest developmental stages thus indicating their probable origin to the west of the Orkney and Shetland Islands and their subsequent transport eastwards by the currents.

Within the North Sea there is no evidence of lemon soles spawning before the beginning of May in any of the three years. Observations (unpublished) by Dr. J. H. Fraser in the 1950s, however, have revealed that small numbers of lemon sole eggs sometimes occur in the Moray Firth and in other northern North Sea grounds in April, and that occasionally, as in April 1952, they may be present in these waters in some concentration. This suggests that the onset of spawning may sometimes be advanced, probably as a result of favourable environmental conditions.

Beginning in the northern half of the Moray Firth in late April or in May, spawning quickly increases in intensity to a peak in June and July, by which time the impulse has spread across the Firth to the southern shore and thence to the coastal grounds of east Aberdeenshire. In the latter area spawning attains its maximum intensity slightly later than in the Moray Firth, and in 1930, for example, appears to have reached its peak in August. In this locality too it is generally continued into September and on a small scale even into October. Still further south, off south-east Scotland and off the north-east coast of England, a study of the developmental stages of the larvae caught from 1929 to 1931 suggests that spawning in the western section of the central North Sea may continue to the end of October and occasionally even into November. These conclusions in regard to the spawning period may be summarized as follows:—

Region	Beginning	Maximum	Completion
West Coast	End of March or beginning of April	April/May	End of July
West of the Orkneys	End of March or beginning of April	May/June	End of August
Shetlands	End of April	May/June	Beginning of September
Moray Firth	End of April or beginning of May	June/July	End of September
Aberdeenshire coast	Mid May	Mid/June, July and August	Beginning of October
West Central North Sea	Mid May	July/August	End of October or beginning of November

In Scottish waters the spawning of the lemon sole begins in the west and spreads northwards and then eastwards into the North Sea. From the northern half of the Moray Firth it extends southwards along the east coast of Scotland. Thus in the Scottish area as a whole the season extends from the end of March to the beginning of November, but it is clear from the number of eggs and larvae taken in the plankton that the heaviest spawning occurs in the north-western North Sea in June, July and August. It also seems probable that the period of heaviest spawning in any locality may vary from year to year by anything up to three weeks.

In the English Channel Ehrenbaum (1909) and Clark (1920) found lemon sole eggs in February and sometimes even in January although the main spawning in this area is probably from March to June.

Little appears to be known of the spawning of this fish in the southern part of the North Sea but the possibility of an early spawning impulse penetrating from the English Channel cannot be entirely disregarded. On the west of Ireland, Holt (1891–1893) found lemon sole eggs in April, May and June.

At Faroe and at Iceland spawning takes place from May to August but in both areas it attains its greatest intensity in June and July.

The Eggs and Larvae

Like other commercially important fishes the lemon sole produces a large number of eggs. Fulton (1890) estimated the number of ova in a fish of $12\frac{1}{2}$ inches at over 150,000 and in another 15 inches at over 670,000. Quite obviously the number varies considerably from fish to fish and would seem to depend on the age and weight of the fish; in general the heavier the fish the greater is the egg production.

The eggs and larvae have been described by a number of biologists including Holt, McIntosh, Petersen and Ehrenbaum. The free floating eggs have a homogeneous yolk without an oil globule. In size they range from 1·13 to 1·45 mm in diameter with an average size decreasing from 1·37 mm in April and May to 1·33 mm in June and to 1·25 mm in July and August.

The development of the lemon sole egg has been studied experimentally and has been described in some detail. Although the development under natural conditions may be regarded as following a somewhat similar course the vertical movements or location of the eggs in the water are not known. Bowman (1914, 1922) has shown that the newly-spawned plaice eggs are

first located at the surface, to which they float upwards after
being shed and fertilized on or near the bottom of the sea. The
development of the embryo is accompanied by a change in
the specific gravity of the egg, which then begins to sink to
deeper water layers where the larva hatches out. In view of the
taxonomic relationship of the plaice and lemon sole, it seems
reasonable to assume that the egg of the lemon sole follows a
somewhat similar course in its development. This assumption
finds some support in the occurrence of newly-hatched lemon
sole larvae at depths well below the surface of the water.

According to Ehrenbaum the incubation period varies with
the temperature of the water; for example, the baby fish hatch
out in eight days at temperatures of 8 to 9·5°C, and in six days
at temperatures of 11·7 to 12·8°C.

On emerging from the egg the larva is from 4·7 to 5·5 mm
long and already reveals traces of black and yellow pigment.
During the first few days of its life the larva subsists on the contents of its yolk-sac and is thus independent of such natural food
as may then be available in the sea. When the yolk is fully
absorbed the little fish must fend for itself. Although the study
of this stage in the life of the baby fish presents obvious difficulties to the research worker and consequently is very
imperfectly known, it is generally considered that it represents a
critical period which may affect the ultimate success or failure
of the year's brood. The presence of an abundant supply of
natural food enables the larva to start feeding immediately the
yolk has been absorbed and thus to avoid any possible interruption to the little fish's continued growth and development.
Ultimately, such conditions would seem to be favourable to the
successful survival of the year's brood and of course to the
benefit of the stock as a whole. On the other hand, the scarcity
or absence of the right kind of food at this time may lead to the
starvation and death of large numbers of larvae with unfortu-
nate results on the stock in subsequent years.

The availability of suitable food, however, is not the only
factor affecting the survival of the young fish. Predation by
their natural enemies and parasitism and disease are biological
factors likely to reduce the numbers of eggs and larvae, but
unfortunately, with the possible exception of the herring and
the plaice, little is known about the vicissitudes of most species

in their larval state. Furthermore, physical features of the water, such as abnormally low temperatures for the time of year, may upset the physiological processes of the little fish and unusual water movements, resulting from the action of winds or currents, may carry the larvae away from their natural habitat. In any of these circumstances the effect on the young brood is likely to be an increase in the natural mortality.

The growth and development of the lemon sole larva has been well known for some time from the work of early investigators. Various developmental stages covering the period of two to three months, from the emergence of the larval fish from the egg to the completion of its pelagic life and its assumption of the demersal life, are illustrated in Figure 4. The features to be noted in these stages are as follows:—

stage 1—the embryo coiled within the egg;

stage 2—the newly-hatched, symmetrical larva with yolk-sac;

stage 3—the larva after the absorption of the yolk-sac, showing the characteristic concavity on the underside caused by the disappearance of the yolk;

stage 4—the growing larva showing the characteristic deepening of the transparent embryonic fins, the elimination of the concavity on the underside and the appearance of the caudal fin;

stage 5—showing the further deepening of the embryonic fins and the appearance of fin rays in the caudal fin.

stage 6—showing the deeper body, the traces of fin-ray supports dorsally and ventrally, the more intense dark-pigment spots on both the fins and the body, the upturning of the notochord (the heterocercal condition) and the growth of the fin rays in the caudal fin;

stage 7—showing the continued deepening of the body, the pronounced heterocercal condition of the notochord, the extension of the fin-rays in the caudal fin, the development of the fin-ray supports and the fin rays, the latter halfway to the margin of the embryonic fins in both the dorsal and ventral fins, and the left eye appearing over the top of the head;

stage 8—showing the deeper body, the complete disappearance
        of the embryonic fin, the separation of the dorsal
        and ventral fins from the caudal fin and the
        continued advance of the eye over the head;

stage 9—the fully metamorphosed, asymmetrical flatfish as it
        takes to life on the sea bottom, showing the forma-
        tion of scales.

LEMON SOLE DEVELOPMENTAL SERIES
FROM EGG TO FIRST BOTTOM STAGE

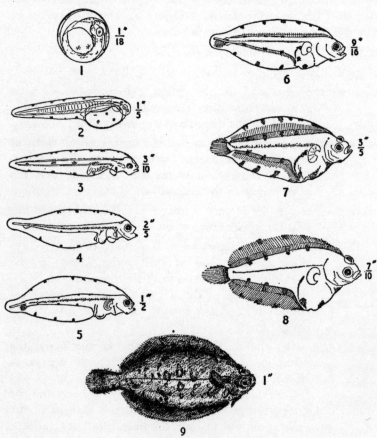

Fig. 4. Lemon Sole developmental series from egg to first bottom stage.

THE METAMORPHOSIS

The last three stages of Figure 4 are of particular interest since they demonstrate the remarkable metamorphosis or change which the pelagic larvae of the lemon sole, and indeed of all flatfishes, undergo before assuming the bottom-living habit. The most striking feature of this change is the movement of one eye over the top of the head to a position close to the other eye. In the lemon sole the left eye moves to the right side, but in some species of flatfish it is the right eye which moves over to the left side. The development of the characteristic, asymmetrical appearance and the assumption of the habit of lying on one side on a surface or on the sea floor, it could be horizontally on the sea floor or vertically on a rock face, is also accompanied by the development of colour on the upper surface and the loss of colour on the underside.

The average lengths of the various developmental stages of the lemon sole during their pelagic or planktonic life vary according to the time of year. In Scottish waters these lengths are greatest in the early part of the season, May and June. Throughout July, August and September there is a slight but progressive diminution in the size of the larvae in each developmental stage (Rae, 1953). This feature has an interesting parallel in the gradual diminution in the average diameter measurement of lemon sole eggs from April to August as demonstrated by Ehrenbaum (1909). The explanation may be that larval growth is greatest early in the season and tends to fall away as the year advances. On the other hand, the gradual rise in the temperature of the water in the North Sea, from April to September, may ensure conditions favourable to the more rapid passage of the larvae through the various developmental stages. At the same time it is worth noting that in localities where the numbers of larvae are exceptionally large, there is a tendency for the average sizes of the various stages to be slightly smaller than in areas where the larvae are sparsely distributed.

THE DRIFT OF THE EGGS AND LARVAE

As constituents of the plankton or floating life, the eggs and larvae of lemon soles, like those of most fishes of commercial

importance, are subject to the movement of the tides and
residual currents. Hydrographers have demonstrated the
persistence of the Atlantic Drift of the Gulf Stream as it moves
from the Atlantic towards the entrances to the North Sea and
beyond to the Norwegian and Arctic Seas. The intricate nature
of the current system within the North Sea has also been revealed in considerable detail (Tait, 1930, 1937). Under its
influence, at least in part, off the north of Shetland, a branch
of the Atlantic Drift enters the North Sea, turns and flows
southwards roughly with its centre along the Greenwich
meridian. On the western edge of the main south-going current
eddies have been shown to exist at a number of points; one of
these in the shape of a rather flattened ellipse lies close to the
east coast of Shetland, another embraces most of the Moray
Firth, and a third occupies the east Scottish Bight from Aberdeen to the Firth of Forth. The surface velocity of the main
currents within the North Sea has been estimated to vary
from a maximum of 12 to 13 miles per day during the late
spring and early summer, to a minimum of 5 to 6 miles per day
during the winter months. It may, of course, be markedly
influenced by wind. As may be expected the speed of the
current at all times decreases with depth. This has been confirmed by recent experiments with bottom current markers
which have indicated an average speed on the sea floor of about
1 mile per day in the last quarter of the year. During the late
spring and summer when the surface speed is greatest the speed
of the bottom current may possibly be rather greater than 1 mile
per day. It is clear, therefore, that the current system of the
north-western North Sea must play an important part in the
dispersal of the eggs and larvae of the lemon sole.

The extent of the dispersal, however, must depend on a
number of factors such as:—

(a) the time between the spawning of the eggs and the
    hatching of the larvae;
(b) the vertical distribution of the eggs in the water layers;
(c) the duration of the planktonic life of the larvae;
(d) the vertical distribution of the larvae in the water layers;
(e) the particular months of the spawning season in which
    the eggs and larvae are pelagic;

(*f*) the distribution of the eggs and larvae relative to the major and subsidiary currents;

(*g*) the direction and strength of the prevailing winds, although, in view of the greater depths at which the larvae are found, this factor probably has less effect on the dispersal of lemon sole larvae than of those of some other species of food fishes.

It has been assumed that the eggs of the lemon sole float upwards to the surface on being shed into the water. It is impossible to say how long they remain in the surface layer, but assuming that they sink with the development of the embryo, as plaice eggs do, they are unlikely to be at the surface for more than 2 to 3 days. During this time the eggs might be carried along at the maximum surface speed of 12 to 13 miles per day if spawned at the beginning of the season. As the eggs sink lower in the water the rate of transport becomes slower. Eggs spawned later in the year would tend to be carried at progressively slower speeds with the gradual running down of the current. With adverse winds their movement may be held up or even reversed.

During the study of the larvae in 1929 to 1931 the depth at which they were caught was investigated. Tow-nets were employed at three depths—surface, midwater and bottom (to a depth limit of 100 metres). This showed that the deepest or "bottom" tow-net caught more larvae than the others (62 to 72% of the total taken by the three nets) and that relatively few were taken in the surface net (2 to 4% of the total). When the records were examined in more detail it was found that the larvae were sparsely distributed at the surface and in the upper water layers to a depth of 30 metres. Below this depth the larvae occurred more frequently and the heaviest concentrations were located at depths from 51 to 100 metres (28 to 54 fathoms). Larvae were taken at depths greater than 100 metres but the numbers declined rapidly with increasing depth.

Despite our knowledge of the velocity of the currents and of the distribution of the eggs and larvae in time, space and depth, it is impossible to be precise about the distance the eggs and young fish are transported during their pelagic life. It seems likely, however, that eggs spawned off the Hebrides in May, for example, may be carried a considerable distance, possibly from 50 to 70 miles, northwards towards Fair Isle and Shetland before they hatch out and the larvae reach the final stage of their development. Within the North Sea, eggs and larvae on the eastern edge of the main south-going current would also appear to be carried some distance into the central North Sea. A southwards drift of eggs and larvae is also evident on the western edge of the main current, particularly off east Aberdeenshire, but on the main lemon sole spawning grounds from Fair Isle to the Firth of Forth, the movement of the plankton is affected to a considerable extent by the various eddies already referred to. These have the effect of carrying eggs and larvae in a clockwise direction and ultimately northwards, possibly in some instances back to where they were spawned. The current system, therefore, serves to concentrate and to retain the young lemon soles within the main centres of distribution of this fish in Scottish waters.

PASSAGE OF THE WINTER BY LARVAE IN THE PELAGIC STATE

The evidence of late spawning by lemon soles at the end of October and at the beginning of November suggests that some larvae may not have time to reach the final stage of their metamorphosis before the end of the year, and that, consequently, some may pass the winter in the pelagic state. Scottish plankton records include larvae at different stages of development taken in December and a young lemon sole without scales which was caught in a bottom tow-net in February; moreover McIntosh has recorded the capture of a larva of 27·5 mm at the surface of the Outer Firth of Forth in May 1890. These records certainly indicate that some larvae may pass the winter in the plankton, but it also seems probable that the number doing so is relatively small.

The incidence of spawning in late August or September, however, also raises the possibility of the young fish taking to life on the sea floor with rudimentary scales. This in turn may have consequences which are likely to affect the age determination of the fish in later years, a subject which will be discussed later.

Chapter IV

AGE DETERMINATION AND AGE COMPOSITION
OF THE STOCKS

Youngest Demersal Fish

Little is known of the earliest bottom phase of the lemon sole's life. The largest post-larval specimen recorded in the plankton for the years 1929 to 1931 was 27·5 mm—that is a little over an inch in length. Fully metamorphosed fish of a rather smaller size, however, have been described and it seems likely that most lemon soles begin their demersal or bottom-living life when they are about an inch long. At this small size the lemon sole is difficult to catch with the normal gears used for sampling young fish stocks on the sea bottom. In about thirty years of research investigations in Scottish waters, largely in those areas where the lemon sole is most plentiful, just over 200 fish of less than two years of age were taken in the small-mesh cover attached to the codend of the otter trawl for research purposes. All of these fish were considerably larger than one inch. This is in marked contrast to the thousands of young plaice and dabs, of up to two inches in length, taken by means of the same gear in the shallow sandy bays of the Scottish coast.

The apparent scarcity of the youngest lemon soles may be explained to some extent by the ease with which these very small, slippery fish can escape through the meshes of nets, aided by the greater opportunities for escape afforded during the hauling of the net from the greater depths at which they are found compared with plaice and dabs. It also seems likely that the rougher nature of the sea bottom frequented by lemon soles provides protection against capture by trawls or dredges.

The depths at which the youngest demersal lemon soles available for examination were caught ranged from 13 to 150 metres (7 to 82 fathoms). In general the youngest fish are taken along with other immature fish of 2 and 3 years of age on grounds normally inhabited by adult lemon soles. Although some adult fish, as will be shown later, follow certain migratory

movements, it would seem that the immature and adolescent
fish remain more or less on the same grounds until they are
approaching maturity.

AGE DETERMINATION IN FISH

The discovery at the beginning of the present century that the
age of fish may be determined by an examination of their
bones or scales represents an important milestone on the path
of fishery research. Maier (1906) was the first to demonstrate
the relationship between the rings on the scales and the age of
lemon soles. Later Dr. A. Bowman, Superintendent of the
Marine Laboratory of the Fishery Board for Scotland, investigated in some detail the use of scales and otoliths or ear-bones
for the age determination of this species. The author was
privileged to share in this work and thus acquired his first
experience of research on the biology of the lemon sole.

The scales of the lemon sole are relatively small and oval, yet
vary in size and shape according to the position they occupy
on the body of the fish. On their surfaces, noticeably on the
transparent part embedded in the skin, numerous concentric
growth accretions, known as sclerites, are arranged in a series
of zones. These zones are distinguished by the varying width
of the individual sclerites. An open zone consisting of a series of
broad sclerites is followed by a close zone or series of narrow
sclerites. Although the transition from close zone to open zone
is sharply marked by a sudden increase in the width of the
individual sclerites, the change from open zone to close zone is
characterized rather by gradual diminution in the width of the
sclerites. Each change from close to open zone is, moreover,
accompanied by the appearance of a new set of radial lines
which extend to the margin of the scale.

All the scales of individual lemon soles caught in any one
season of the year are in the same growth phase, and scales from
different fish in any month are also found to be more or less in
the same growth phase. The change from the close to the open
zone appears earlier in some fish than in others, even on the
same ground. In the north-western North Sea the time of this
transition varies on the different grounds. South of Rattray
Head, where, as will be shown later, lemon soles grow most
rapidly, the open phase makes its appearance in the second

half of February, but, proceeding northwards, the appearance of the open phase on the scales is delayed so that round Shetland, where it will be shown growth is poorest, the open phase in some fish may not appear until the beginning of June.

It is clear that, in general, the open phase begins to appear on the scales from March to May, thus coinciding with the approach of more favourable conditions for feeding and growth. Accordingly, the close phase on the scale represents the slow growth of the fish during the winter, and the open phase the rapid growth of the late spring and summer. A complete cycle of one close and one open phase on the scale, therefore, represents one year's growth in the life of the fish and thus by counting these annual growth cycles one obtains the age of the fish.

SCALE SURVEYS

In view of the variation in the size and shape of scales from different parts of the fish, scale surveys were carried out to ascertain whether all scales were equally reliable for age-reading purposes. In these surveys every fifth scale was examined along the lateral line from the head to the tail, and from each of these lateral line scales every fifth scale was also examined in rows stretching obliquely backwards and outwards towards the dorsal and ventral fins. Scales were also taken from the head, the fins and the tail. Passing outwards from the lateral line, both dorsally and ventrally, a gradual diminution was noted in the size of the scales. This was associated with a gradual reduction in the number of sclerites laid down during the first year of life until near the base of the fins the first winter ring disappeared completely. The first winter ring was also found to be missing from the scales taken from the fins and the tail, but the head scales, though small, nearly all had the full complement of annual rings. These surveys demonstrated the unsuitability of scales taken from certain parts of the fish and at the same time indicated the desirability of taking scale samples for age determination from the lateral line at a point about two-thirds of the length backwards from the head. At this position, known as the "patch", the scales attain their greatest size and almost certainly include the maximum number of sclerites in the first winter ring. It would appear that the development of the scales on the young fish begins on the "patch" and spreads outwards in all directions over the body of the fish. The recognition of these lateral line scales is facilitated by a characteristic ridge running diagonally across the scale and by the maximum development of the radial lines from the beginning of the various open phases of growth.

THE USE OF OTOLITHS IN AGE DETERMINATION

The possible alternative use of otoliths, or ear-bones, for age determination was also examined. The otoliths of lemon soles, however, are small and although the annual rings are generally clearly distinguishable during the early years of the fish, the proximity of the later rings is such that considerable difficulty may be experienced in distinguishing them. Accordingly, for this reason, and also because far greater numbers of scale samples than of otoliths can be collected and examined in any given time, it was decided to rely mainly on scales for the age determination of lemon soles.

DIFFICULTIES ENCOUNTERED IN SCALE READING
Indeterminate Centres

Despite the general excellence of lemon sole scales for age-reading purposes various difficulties are experienced from time to time and from one locality to another. The first of these is the problem of indeterminate centres in which growth sclerites appear either never to have been laid down, as a result of the larval fish passing the first winter in the pelagic state, or if laid down, to have been damaged by the reabsorption by the fish of some of the material of the scales. The latter difficulty can usually be overcome by searching for more suitable scales in the sample since the reabsorption of scale material is not evident on all scales.

The number of lemon soles with scales exhibiting the absence of the first winter ring, referred to on p. 49, is known to vary from year to year. This feature was found during the examination of scales in the mid-1930s to be particularly prevalent on the scales of lemon soles spawned in 1930. The study of the distribution of the larvae of that year revealed a particularly heavy spawning, off the Aberdeenshire coast, which extended from August well into September. Although the young lemon soles resulting from this late spawning almost certainly had time to metamorphose and take to living on the sea floor before the end of the year, it is doubtful if the scales of the youngest of them had time to add more than a few sclerites of the first winter close phase to their growth. In some examples of this nature, it is often possible with sufficient experience to recognize the slight trace of the first winter from evidence of a few sclerites, but in others, the existence of an earlier ring is mainly deduced from the width of the "first" winter ring (in reality the second winter ring) visibly on the scale. These observations are demonstrated by the following results of the analysis of a sample of lemon sole of the 1930 brood from the Aberdeenshire coast grounds:—

first winter ring present (1) on all scales 73·1%
                           (2) on lateral line scales
                               only 17·6%
first winter ring absent (1) centre to second winter
                               ring wide 6·5%
                           (2) centre to second winter
                               ring narrow 2·8%

The age analysis of these fish was checked by examining the otoliths in which the first winter ring is always identifiable, evidently because the formation of the otolith begins early in the life of the larval fish, while the beginning of scale formation is delayed until near the end of the metamorphosis. It should also be noted that of several year-classes examined from 1931 to 1936, the 1930 brood included the highest proportion of fish with doubtful scale centres. In other broods the proportion was smaller, and in fish of the 1931 brood none was found to have really doubtful scales. Because of this and from the evidence of the distribution in time of the 1931 larvae, it has been concluded that this brood was the product of a relatively early spawning. It would appear, therefore, that a relatively high proportion of scales with indeterminate or doubtful centres in any brood is indicative of a relatively late spawning.

False Rings

Another difficulty encountered in the interpretation of the age of lemon soles from scales is the occurrence of false rings. These are characterized by the appearance of a few sclerites with

rather ragged outlines in the midst of the open zone or summer
phase. After the interruption, the sclerites resume their normal
open formation. These false rings are more frequent on scales
of lemon soles from Shetland grounds (14 to 24%) than on
those taken south of Rattray Head (2 to 12%). They are not
equally prominent on all the scales of any individual fish and
indeed may not be present on some. On rare occasions two
false rings may occur in one year's growth. False rings never
appear in the scale growth of the first two years. Few have been
recorded in the third year's growth but in general they begin
to appear regularly in the fourth year. In some fish false rings
may appear in the midst of the fourth and sixth years' growth,
but not in the fifth. From the available evidence on this problem, it has been concluded that false rings are associated with
spawning. Normally the act of spawning is an exhausting
process which seriously affects the condition of the fish. This
in itself may be sufficient to arrest, temporarily, the growth
of the fish and consequently the growth of the scale. It seems
more likely, however, that false rings are caused by a combination of factors involving severe effects of spawning, local or
general scarcity of food at a time when the fish's body re-
sources are in urgent need of rehabilitation and perhaps even
unfavourable environmental conditions in the sea. Moreover, the shock effect of this experience on the fish may be all
the greater because it occurs when feeding and growth are
rapidly mounting to their summer maxima. There is also,
however, some evidence, for example from recaptured tagged
fish, that false rings may be caused by shock or injury through
contact with fishing gear.

Age Composition of Lemon Sole Stocks

The age-composition of the lemon sole stocks in Scottish home
waters and elsewhere was investigated in the period between
the two wars. The material utilized for this purpose consisted
of the fish caught by the Scottish research vessel *Explorer* from
1922 to 1939. Although these records included only from about
700 to 2500 fish per year, they were obtained from a very wide
area in the northern and central North Sea and off the West
Coast of Scotland, at all times of the year. They were also all
procured by means of the same fishing gear—an otter trawl

with a small-mesh cover over the codend to retain the smallest fish. This material was, therefore, considered more truly representative of the lemon sole stocks in the area investigated than samples available from commercial sources, in which the element of bias must inevitably operate in any predominantly incidental fishery such as that of the lemon sole.

Number of Exploitable Year-classes

The analysis of the annual catches by the *Explorer* in Scottish waters, reproduced in Table VI, reflects the age composition of the stocks during the period between the wars. Table VI reveals a number of interesting features. It confirms the scarcity of the youngest fish, up to two years of age, in the catches referred to on p. 47. It also shows that lemon soles of up to fifteen years of age appear fairly regularly in the North Sea catches, while two exceptionally old fish were identified, each about nineteen years old, one in 1922 and the other, surprisingly enough, in 1936. The research vessel catches include lemon soles from ten to fifteen different year-groups, but these include fish of less than two years of age which are rarely if ever caught by commercial vessels. Consequently, the number of year-classes available for exploitation by fishermen at any time varies from nine to thirteen. Pursuing this aspect of the subject the period has been subdivided as follows:—

Years	No. of Exploitable Age Groups	Average
1922–1926	12, 13, 12, 13, 12	12·4
1927–1931	13, 13, 12, 10, 11	11·8
1932–1936	11, 9, 10, 10, 12	10·4
1937–1939	12, 12, 11	11·7

This reveals a gradual reduction in the average number of fishable year-classes in Scottish waters up to the middle of the third period, which may be attributed to the growing intensity of commercial fishing between the wars and also to some extent to the concomitant increase in the lemon sole catch by British fishermen to its maximum in the mid-1930s. However,

the sudden increase in the number of age-groups in commercially exploitable fish, which occurred in 1936 and was
apparently maintained until 1939, is not easily explained. It
may possibly indicate some relaxation of the intensity of fishing
for lemon soles, although the incidental nature of the fishery
for this species and the lack of evidence of any appreciable
decrease in the overall fishing effort in Scottish waters in those
years do not support this view.

Relative Strengths of the Broods

Table VI also indicates the relative strengths of the various
broods contributing to each year's catch. Certain broods clearly
stand out as providing greater proportions of the annual catches
than others. In no year, however, did the contribution by any of
the most prolific broods exceed 35% of the total catch. At the
same time the poorest brood, that of 1929, in its most productive year, provided just over 13% of the year's catch. Five
broods, those of 1921, 1922, 1926, 1930 and 1933 accounted
for 30% or more of the catch in one or two years of their
existence and may, therefore, on this evidence be regarded as
the most successful broods contributing to the stocks between
the wars. Another five, those of 1919, 1924, 1929, 1931 and
1932, failed to provide 20%, even in their most productive
year, so that they must be regarded as the least successful
broods.

These proportions of the catch, provided by each year-class,
indicate the relative strengths of the broods. It is difficult, in
view of the relatively small numbers of fish available and the
relatively large numbers of year-classes represented annually,
to estimate the strength of the broods in more absolute terms.
However, an attempt has been made to calculate the average
numbers of lemon soles caught per ten hours' fishing during the
fourth, fifth, sixth and seventh years of the life of each brood,
these being regarded as the most productive years in the
commercial fishery. The results of this calculation are represented in Figure 5. By this means the six outstanding broods
in order of importance appear to be those of 1922, 1921, 1920,
1933, 1930 and 1926. This agrees with the previous assessment
on the basis of numbers of fish and percentages of the total
but with the addition of the 1920 brood. From a knowledge

of the build-up of stocks during the first war and their subsequent exploitation by fishermen, it seems likely that the apparent strengths of the various broods, as evident from Figure 5, were to some extent affected by the growing intensity of commercial fishing. In other words, the increase in the intensity of fishing combined with improvements in fishing gear during the 1920s gradually reduced the stocks and brought about the state of over-fishing prevalent during the 1930s, which is reflected in the somewhat lower catches per unit of fishing time of the later broods in Figure 5. It is interesting to note, however, that the weakest broods, on the relative percentage basis, are the same as in Figure 5, with the 1929 brood appearing as the weakest of all by each method.

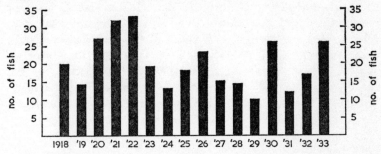

FIG. 5. Brood strengths, based on average numbers caught per 10 hours' fishing during the four most productive years (fourth to seventh) of the Lemon Sole's life.

Figure 5 also reveals that over the whole Scottish area the ratio of the most successful brood to the least successful is somewhere in the region of 3 or 4 to 1. If the records are considered on a regional basis the ratio is somewhat greater— for example on grounds to the south of Rattray Head it is approximately 5 to 1. These are remarkably low ratios if compared with the corresponding ratio of 60 to 1 for haddock in the North Sea as a whole. The explanation may lie in the marked differences in the biology of the two species. Although both species are predominantly natives of medium depths and geographically occupy the same grounds, the haddock spawns in the spring, mainly in the deeper water of the northern North Sea, where conditions at that time of year may frequently be unfavourable to the survival of the larvae. On the other hand, the lemon sole is mainly a summer spawner on grounds nearer to the Scottish coast, where environmental conditions, both physical and biological, are at that time likely to be more favourable for the larval fish. Another factor which may possibly help to account for the smaller annual fluctuations in the lemon sole broods is the prolonged spawning period of the species. As already observed this lasts from the end of March or beginning of April to the end of October or beginning of November, and even in the North Sea, off the Scottish east coast, it extends over at least six months. Moreover, spawning may be concentrated locally in this area at any time from June to August, so that heavy mortalities among larvae at any time or in any locality are likely to be cancelled out by successful survival at some other time or place. In contrast the spawning of the haddock though covering a wider area than the lemon sole, is nevertheless, because of the numbers involved, more concentrated, as well as being confined to a shorter period. These features suggest that the haddock may be more vulnerable than the lemon sole during its larval existence, and this may account for the far greater fluctuations in its brood strengths.

Age at First Maturity

Lemon soles do not all spawn for the first time at the same age. Indeed the advent of first maturity of the members of any one brood may be spread over a considerable period of years. All lemon soles of two years of age or less may be regarded as immature but from two years onwards maturing and ripe fish appear in increasing numbers. Male lemon soles clearly mature earlier than the females. Rather more than half the male fish in any brood spawn for the first time in their third year of life but the percentage of females of the same age-group doing so is negligible. By the time they are four years old most male fish have spawned at least once, while at least half of the females are still in the immature state. At five years of age most of the female lemon soles have reached maturity. In some localities a very small percentage of the fish may not reach the adult state until later, for example immature males and females have been found as late as their seventh and eighth years respectively.

Chapter V

GROWTH AND FOOD

THE GROWTH OF THE LEMON SOLE

It is clear from the differences in the sizes of fully-grown
fish that the rate of growth varies considerably from one
species to another. What may not be so generally known is that
growth rates also vary within a particular species. The late
Dr. Harold Thompson (1928) was one of the first to demonstrate this in his researches on the haddock in Scottish waters.
He showed that the local variations in the rate of growth of
this species in the North Sea and neighbouring grounds were
linked with the depth, the temperature of the water and the
nature of the food supply.

Variations in the growth of lemon soles have also been
demonstrated in the North Sea and elsewhere. The method
employed was the correlation of length measurements of the
fish with their age as determined from scale examination.
In this way a series of average sizes was calculated for each
quarter of the year in different localities; by comparing the
various averages and by combining those which were approximately similar an overall impression was obtained of lemon
sole growth in Scottish waters (see Figure 6). The area of most
successful growth lies in the western half of the central North
Sea adjacent to the Scottish and north-east English coasts.
In this region growth is identified by the Firth of Forth type.
Proceeding north-eastwards from the Firth of Forth zone a
succession of zones of gradually diminishing growth is encountered which ends in an area of very poor growth on the
edge of the deeper water to the north of Muckle Flugga at the
northern end of Shetland. Curves representing the rates of
growth in the six North Sea zones are illustrated in Figure 7.

From Muckle Flugga the zone of poor growth extends both
eastwards to the Norwegian Deep and south-westwards along
the continental shelf to the offshore banks lying to the south of
the Outer Hebrides. This area includes the small island of

North Rona in the vicinity of which lemon soles exhibit an exceptionally slow rate of growth which may be regarded as typifying the slowest growth for this species recorded in the north-east Atlantic. Comparable average sizes for this locality are shown in Figure 7. In the coastal waters on the west of Scotland growth is more successful, particularly in the sheltered

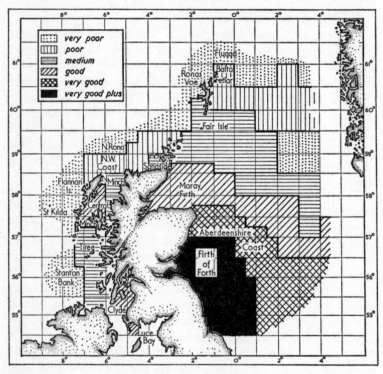

Fig. 6. Lemon Sole growth zones.

waters of the Minch and Firth of Clyde, but nowhere does it compare with the Firth of Forth type.

Lemon sole growth at Faroe compares very favourably with that of the North Sea. In one locality, north and west of Myggenaes, the relatively young stock exhibits a rate of growth superior to that of any other locality in the north-east Atlantic (see Figure 7). Off the north and north-eastern coasts of the islands growth closely resembles the Firth of Forth type and round the southern islands the moderate rate of growth is closest to the Fair Isle type of Scottish waters. Very poor growth occurs in only one locality, on Faroe Bank, where the type is comparable with that of North Rona.

In Faxa Bay, Iceland, lemon sole growth is moderately good and approaches closest to the Moray Firth type of the North Sea. Data from the south coast of Iceland are not so plentiful, but such average sizes as are available indicate growth rates comparable with or slightly inferior to that of Faxa Bay.

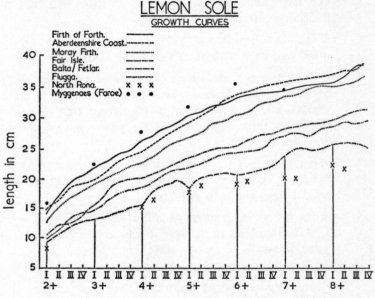

FIG. 7. Growth curves based on average quarterly lengths of the different age groups.

Figure 7 summarizes in graphical form the lemon sole growth rates of the North Sea and indicates the two extremes of good and poor growth experienced in the north-east Atlantic. It is remarkable that within a single species growth may be twice as great in one area as in another.

Maximum Size

These investigations revealed a remarkable range in the growth rates of lemon soles within the three main centres of distribution in the north-east Atlantic. This is all the more surprising when one considers that the species on the whole is slow-growing in comparison with some other food fishes. Lemon soles of up to 48 cm (18·9 in) regularly occur in commercial catches but few exceed this size. Since published information relating to the maximum size attained by this species is inadequate it seems appropriate to refer to the following extra large lemon soles which have been recorded at the Marine Laboratory, Aberdeen:—

1. 67·0 cm (26·4 in), caught in the Inner Firth of Forth, in 8 fathoms, on 9th January, 1907;

2. 61·0 cm (24 in), caught at Iceland, 12th January, 1923, sex male, age from scales—21 years (see Plate II);

3. 57·2 cm (22·5 in), breadth 32 cm, trawled 4 miles offshore between the Easter and Wester Horns, Iceland, in 28 to 36 fathoms, on 22nd May, 1946, female three-quarters ripe, age from scales about 23 years, gutted weight 2949 gm (6½ lb);

4. 57·0 cm (22·4 in), trawled 10 miles off Fraserburgh, 13th February, 1964, sex male, approaching 15 years of age, weight 2230 gm (4 lb 14½ oz);

5. 55·3 cm (21·75 in), caught 24 miles ESE of Aberdeen on 15th September, 1934, weight ungutted 2069 gm (4 lb 9 oz), age 13+ (? 14+) years;

6. 52·5 cm, caught 19 miles SE of Aberdeen on 15th July, 1930, female, weight ungutted 1842 gm (4 lb 1 oz), gutted 1758 gm (3 lb 14 oz);

7. 51·0 cm, caught off the Bass Rock, Outer Firth of Forth, 4th March, 1904;

8. 50·8 cm, caught off Rattray Head, Aberdeenshire, 18th July, 1935, weight ungutted 2041 gm (4½ lb);

9. 50·0 cm, caught on Smith Bank, Moray Firth, 1st July, 1920;

10. 50·0 cm, caught east of Shetland, 7th June, 1928, age 12 years;

11. 49·0 cm, caught in the Dornoch Firth, 25th June, 1920.

Comparison of the Growth of Male and Female Fish

In considering the growth of lemon soles no distinction has
been drawn between male and female fish. This aspect of
the subject was investigated in Icelandic lemon soles between
the two wars (Rae, 1948). Briefly the growth rates of the sexes
are about the same during the first few years of life. After
reaching maturity, however, the female fish appear to grow
more quickly than the males, so that in fish of from 10 to 17 years
of age the difference in the average sizes of the sexes (age for
age) ranged from 3·6 to 8·3 cm with a tendency for this difference to increase with age.

Sex Ratio

This characteristic of the growth, which incidentally has also
been observed in other fish, may be associated in some way
with the marked change in the sex ratio which occurs with
advancing age. In the early years of life male and female
lemon soles, as in halibut and other species (Rae, 1959),
appear in the stocks in about equal numbers. Later, usually
with the advent of maturity, the females begin to outnumber
the males—a feature which becomes progressively more evident
as the fish grow older.

Why this should be so is not fully understood but it may
be that the act of spawning annually takes a heavier toll of the
males than of the females. This has been confirmed in at least
one fish—the salmon—in which losses among male kelts every
year are considerably greater than among the females. If this
should be true of the lemon sole the death rate from natural
causes will be greater among adult male fish than among adult
females. Furthermore, because males, on an average, spawn for
the first time from one to two years earlier and at correspond-
ingly smaller sizes than the females, it follows that males must
be suffering losses from the effects of spawning well before the
females first reach maturity. Bearing in mind, too, that the
faster-growing fish in any age-group are among the first to
mature, it would seem that several factors contribute to an
earlier and more effective thinning of the adult male fish than
of the females. This might well have the effect of decreasing
the average sizes of the males in the various size-groups

and thus give the impression that females grow faster than males.

Possible Causes of Variations in Growth Rate

In seeking an explanation of the different rates of growth of lemon soles an attempt was made, in the light of Dr. Thompson's work on haddock, to link the differences in the North Sea with the depth and the temperature of the water. In the areas of the most successful lemon sole growth, the western part of the central North Sea (see Figure 6), the depths range from the shallow water of the Firth of Forth to 50 fathoms on the western side of the Gut. Passing from the Aberdeenshire coast growth zone through the Moray Firth to Fair Isle, the rate of growth becomes slower as the average depth of the water increases, but despite the increasing range of depth within the zones the growth throughout each zone remains remarkably true to type. The increase in the average depth of grounds to the east and north of Shetland, 60 to 90 fathoms, is accompanied by a marked decline in the growth rate. Outside the North Sea moderately good lemon sole growth occurs in the Minch in depths ranging from 60 to 90 fathoms, while very poor growth characterizes this species in the vicinity of North Rona, where medium depths of 30 to 60 fathoms predominate.

At Faroe, the very successful growth pertaining to grounds surrounding the northern isles and the moderate growth in the vicinity of the southern isles both occur within depths of 30 to 60 fathoms, while very slow growth on Faroe Bank is recorded from depths of 60 to 100 fathoms. In Icelandic waters a dense concentration of lemon soles is located in the southern half of Faxa Bay, largely in waters of less than 20 fathoms, but the species is also caught in quantity in other parts of the bay to a depth of 80 fathoms. Throughout the bay the growth rate is moderately good.

Although there is some slight indication of a correlation between growth rate and depth at the deeper limits of the lemon sole's distribution, there is no consistent evidence of this over the main depth range of the species. Growth seems to vary irrespective of depth.

Similarly no relationship has been established between growth rate and water temperatures. Good growth is recorded in regions where the temperatures vary considerably through-out the year, as in the Firth of Forth, and also where the variation is relatively slight, as round the Faroes. Slow growth may also occur under varying temperature conditions, for example in certain lochs and fjords and in some northern localities of the North Sea, as well as in places where the temperature range is narrow, as at North Rona and on Faroe Bank.

The salinity range over the lemon sole's distribution does not vary to any great extent, but here, too, there is no evidence of a link between salinity and growth rate, the best growth occurring both in the high salinities of Faroese waters and in the relatively low salinities of the Firth of Forth.

It is obvious, therefore, that some other factor or factors must account for the differences that occur in the growth rate of lemon soles. With this in mind a detailed investigation of the food of lemon soles was carried out in each of the three main centres of distribution in the late 1930s.

THE FOOD OF LEMON SOLES

The feeding habits and the composition of the food of the lemon sole differ in several ways from those of other fishes. Unlike some species the lemon sole is largely a seasonal feeder; very few fish take food in the first two months of the year, but from March onwards feeding increases rapidly and except for a slight recession observed in the adult fish in May, continues to reach a maximum in June and July. Thereafter, a gradual decline sets in; the number of empty stomachs increases and the amount of food consumed by the individual fish decreases until, in December, feeding stops almost completely. The changes in the feeding cycle of the lemon sole throughout the year is perhaps most effectively demonstrated by Figure 8 in which the volumes of food per 100 stomachs in each month and for each size-group are shown graphically.

In December all but a small porportion of lemon sole stomachs (about 3%) are completely devoid of food. Moreover, at this time the intestines, which are long and turgid when the fish are feeding, become completely empty and shrink to a fraction of their normal size. These features emphasize the comprehensive nature of the stoppage which seems to indicate that the lemon sole experiences a condition resembling some form of hibernation. This view, incidentally, finds some support from the natural scarcity of lemon soles in commercial catches during the winter months. Why this arrestment of feeding should be so marked in the lemon sole, while appearing

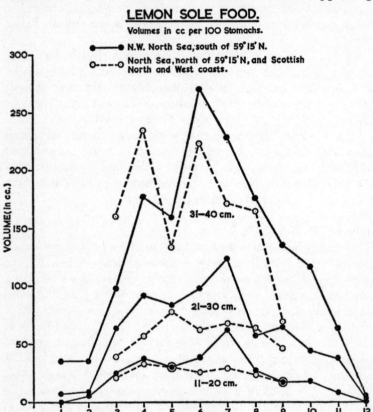

FIG. 8. The feeding cycle of Lemon Soles in 10 cm size-groups.

much less obvious in related species of flatfish and non-existent in some roundfish is not readily apparent. It may, however, be related to the specialized nature of the food or to some feature of the food supply which, as yet, is not understood.

The lemon sole has also been known for some time to differ from most other species of commercial food fishes in its preference for a diet of polychaete worms. In order to study the food of the species in more detail and to investigate any possible relationship between food and growth, the contents of more than 5000 lemon sole stomachs were examined. The material was collected according to the size of the fish, in 10 cm groups, and for convenience it was considered on a regional basis as closely related as possible to the growth zones. The results are broadly illustrated by means of histograms, in Figures 9 and 10. In Figure 9 the numbers of stomachs containing each of the main food types are expressed as percentages of the total numbers of stomachs containing recognizable food. Altogether eleven main types of food were identified including, in addition to polychaetes, crustaceans, molluscs, echinoderms, coelenterates, nemerteans, gephyreans, ascidians, polyzoans, fish and red algae. The last three types, however, were represented merely by traces, or only on rare occasions, and consequently have not been included in Figures 9 and 10.

Polychaete Worms

Polychaete worms are clearly the predominant food type of lemon soles. As Figure 9 shows, they exceed in importance each of the other types in each region and in each size-group, with the exception of the smallest fish off the north and west coasts of Scotland, where they share the position of prime importance with small crustaceans. The overall importance of polychaetes to the lemon sole is further emphasized by Figure 10, in which the volumetric analysis of the food shows that they provide an even greater proportion of the food than the frequency of their occurrence in the stomachs suggests. In all size-groups and in all regions, except for the larger fish on grounds to the south of Rattray Head and to some extent also in the Moray Firth, polychaetes provide the bulk of the food. On these southern grounds the larger lemon soles find suitable alternatives, chiefly in the form of the anthozoan genus *Cerianthus* and certain lamellibranchs and nudibranchs.

Other Types

Although the frequency of occurrence records indicate a fairly high proportion of fish of all sizes feeding on crustaceans in all regions, the forms preyed upon vary from one region to

LEMON SOLE FOOD.

Frequency Percentages.

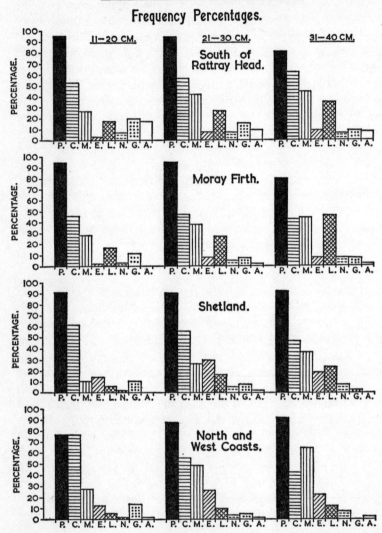

FIG. 9. Frequency of occurrence of the various types in the stomachs: percentages calculated on the number of stomachs containing recognisable food.

another. On southern grounds they consist largely of small eupagurids, and on northern grounds of amphipods and larval decapods, none of which is of much importance volumetrically except for small fish in the north and west. Many of the molluscs eaten are also small forms such as chitons and young lamellibranchs and gastropods, but the larger lemon soles in some localities prey on much larger bivalves by biting off the protruding parts such as mantle fringes and siphons. Most of the echinoderms eaten by lemon soles consist of small ophiuroids. This type is taken more frequently by the smaller and medium-sized fish, especially on Shetland and north-western grounds. The importance of the coelenterate *Cerianthus* to the larger lemon soles is largely confined to southern grounds (south of Rattray Head and Moray Firth). The value of this type as an alternative food in these areas is emphasized by its relatively high volumetric measurement in Figure 10. On northern grounds most of the coelenterates eaten are hydroids, many of them represented merely by traces, which may have been ingested accidentally with other food. The remaining food types, nemerteans, gephyreans, and ascidians are relatively unimportant, although they are eaten by all sizes of fish, sometimes in particular localities, in all regions. Some typical organisms in the lemon sole's diet are featured in Figure 11.

Relationship between Growth and Food

From these observations and with the help of Figures 9 and 10, it is clear that differences exist in the food of lemon soles in the four regions. As these regions broadly represent the different growth zones it seems that some correlation exists between growth and food. This relationship becomes even more obvious if the composition of the food is considered in still greater detail —for example the polychaetes preyed upon by lemon soles on the southern grounds, where growth is most successful, consist predominantly of sedentary types in which the families of the Terebellidae, Serpulidae and Sabellariidae are outstanding. In the northern and western regions, where lemon sole growth is slow, on the other hand, the polychaetes eaten include higher proportions of errant types, among which the Aphroditidae and Eunicidae are prominent.

LEMON SOLE FOOD.

Volumetric Percentages.

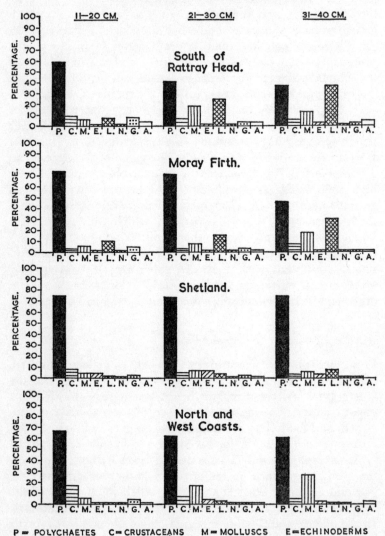

P = POLYCHAETES   C = CRUSTACEANS   M = MOLLUSCS   E = ECHINODERMS

L = COELENTERATES   N = NEMERTEANS   G = GEPHYREANS   A = ASCIDIANS

FIG. 10. Volumetric analysis of the stomach contents: quantities of each type
expressed as percentages of the total volume.

The differences may be summarized as follows:—

1. where the growth rate is good the food consists mainly of sedentary polychaetes, small decapod crustaceans (eupagurids), lamellibranchs and gastropods (including nudibranchs) and *Cerianthus;*
2. where growth is poor the food consists mainly of polychaetes (including a high proportion of errant forms), amphipods, small molluscs (chitons and the smaller Patellidae) and ophiuroids or brittlestars.

The regional variations in the food of lemon soles may be illustrated by Figure 12 which shows the incidence in the stomachs of four representative sub-types.

Availability of Food

These differences alone are probably sufficient to influence growth rate, but other factors remain to be considered, namely density of population and the amount of food available. Although the bulk of commercial landings of lemon soles is obtained from grounds to the east of the Scottish mainland, appreciable quantities are also caught in Shetland waters. As may be expected small lemon soles predominate in the catches from the latter area. This has been confirmed by research vessel records in which more than 56% of the total may consist of undersized fish as compared with the equivalent of 22% for grounds in the Moray Firth and south of Rattray Head. This difference is due not to a younger stock of fish but to the slower rate of growth. Moreover, the average quantity of food found in the stomachs of lemon soles in each 10 cm size-group from the Shetland area has been found to be smaller than the corresponding quantities from southern grounds in the North Sea (see Figure 8). If growth is affected by density of stock and food supply it follows that any reduction in the numbers of a stock should result in improved growth provided the food supply remains the same, and, conversely, any improvement in the food supply should also give rise to better growth in a stable population.

It has been concluded, therefore, that the nature of the food and the quantity available for the stock on the ground are prime factors in determining the growth rate of lemon soles.

LEMON SOLE   FOOD   TYPE.

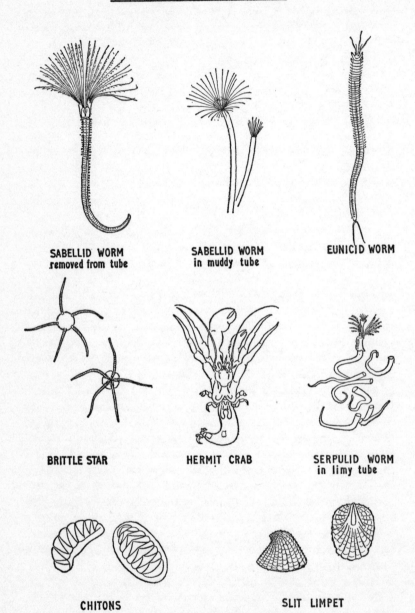

FIG. 11. Lemon Sole food types.

Towards the lower limits of the lemon sole's vertical range it would seem that depth also has some limiting effect on the rate of growth, although this factor should perhaps be regarded more as limiting the distribution of the species.

General Characteristics of the Lemon Sole Food

Although from 76 to 95% of lemon soles (depending on the size of the fish and the region in which they are caught) feed on polychaete worms, the food as a whole includes a remarkable variety of different organisms in each of the main food types. No fewer than 22 polychaete families, including at least 60 different species, were identified in the stomachs. Similarly, at least 20 species of crustaceans (10 of them decapods), 15 molluscs, 12 echinoderms and 4 gephyreans, all small animals, were recognized in the food analysis. Despite the long list of individual organisms eaten by lemon soles, many of them have been recognized but rarely, and most of the food consists of a relatively small number of different animals. For example, of the 60 polychaetes identified less than a quarter appear regularly or frequently in the food. Of these, seven species, the serpulids, *Serpula vermicularis*, *Hydroides norvegica* and *Pomatoceros triqueter*, the terebellids, *Thelepus cincinnatus* and *Lanice conchilega*, and the eunicids, *Onuphis conchylega* and *Hyalinoecia tubicola*, are by far the commonest and, presumably, the most important food items to the lemon sole.

The almost complete absence of fish from the lemon sole's diet is interesting because most of the common food fishes in British waters feed heavily on fish at some time in their lives. The lemon sole by feeding predominantly on polychaetes would appear to avoid interspecific competition for food to a considerable extent. At least one other species, the witch, feeds heavily on polychaetes but, because the witch is a native of muddy bottoms, the polychaetes in its food are markedly different from those eaten by the lemon sole.

Although the lemon sole certainly feeds on organisms which are also eaten by other fish, many of the items in its diet are small in size since, with its characteristically small mouth, the fish is incapable of ingesting anything bigger. In this way it again tends to avoid competition by preying on the smallest and possibly the youngest members of the decapod crustaceans,

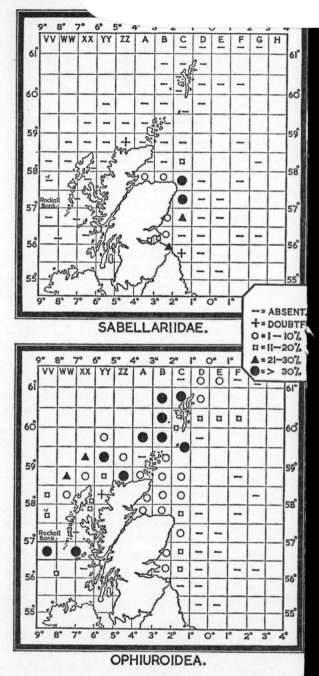

SABELLARIIDAE.

—= ABSENT
+ = DOUBTF
O = 1 — 10%
◻ = 11—20%
▲ = 21–30%
● = > 30%

OPHIUROIDEA.

Fig. 12. Lemon Sole food: the i

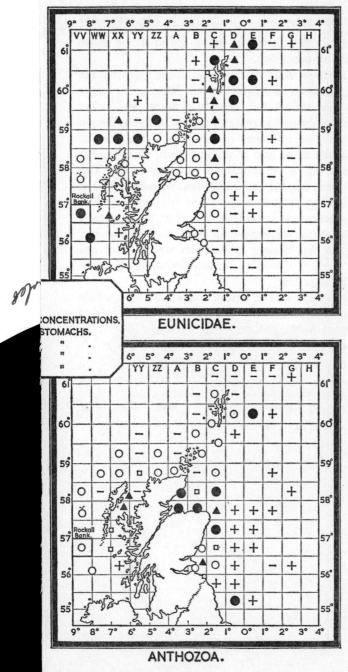

EUNICIDAE.

ANTHOZOA.

four sub-types in the stomachs.

ᴄ
th
teeth
for thi
feeds by
of fish in a
and investig
indicate that
lemon sole tha

An outstandi
is its sedentary ...., nature. In this respect it
is in marked contrast to the mobile types, such as fish, natant
decapods and cephalopods, preyed upon by many other species.
Consequently, whereas some fish may feed by waiting for their
prey to come to them, the lemon sole must necessarily move
around in search of its food. This characteristic would seem, to
some extent, to be borne out by the alert appearance and somewhat restless behaviour of lemon soles in aquaria.

Chapter VI

TAGGING EXPERIMENTS ON LEMON SOLES

The tagging of fish, for the purpose of studying their movements and other aspects of their life and biology, is a technique which has been employed in Scottish fishery research since about 1890. In these early days the experiments were mainly carried out on plaice, which proved to be particularly suitable because of their ability to survive the treatment involved. Later it was discovered that lemon soles were also reasonably hardy and a series of marking or tagging experiments was initiated with this fish shortly after the first war. The fish were liberated with button-like discs attached to the base of their dorsal fin. By this means they were identified when caught by commercial fishermen, who were asked to return them to the laboratory. For their trouble the fishermen received a small monetary reward, together with information relating to the liberation of the fish and its subsequent movements and growth. Nearly 8000 lemon soles were tagged and of these just over a thousand, 13%, were recovered up to a year after the final experiment.

This work had some interesting results. In the first place it provided incontrovertible evidence of the validity of the use of scales as a means of age determination in fish. Scales removed from the fish at liberation and again on return to the laboratory were compared by microscopic examination. Invariably the scales of fish which had been at liberty for a year or more revealed the addition of one or more winter rings, comparable with the period of liberty (see Plate III).

Tagging experiments also showed that the great majority (about 80%) of lemon soles remained within a radius of 30 miles of their position of liberation. Even if allowance is made for the possible movement of others at a later date, if they had survived, the records suggest that the species as a whole does not undertake extensive migrations. Concentrations of fish are of course known to occur for spawning purposes but in general these would seem to be comparatively local in character.

Many of the non-migrant fish were free for comparatively short periods but some were at liberty for long periods. One fish, liberated at a position about 8 miles off Aberdeen, was away for nearly 10 years before being recaptured within a few miles of its liberation point. Although it cannot be stated with certainty that this fish did not move away from the area in the interval between liberation and recapture, the results from other taggings in the vicinity seem to suggest that, if it had moved, either it could have gone northwards, in which case it would not have returned south, or it might have been caught up in and made one or more contranatant circuits of the mid-east Scottish Eddy between the Aberdeenshire coast and the Firth of Forth.

The Extent and Direction of Lemon Sole Migrations

The remaining 20% of the recaptured tagged fish were found to have moved thirty miles or more from their point of liberation. For the purpose of the investigation these were regarded as migrants. With few exceptions the migrant fish within the North Sea moved in a northerly direction towards the Moray Firth, Fair Isle or Shetland, depending on where they were set free. Migrant lemon soles tagged in the vicinity of Fair Isle and the Shetland Isles on the other hand, followed quite a different course and were recaptured to the southwest, sometimes in the vicinity of Cape Wrath or the Butt of Lewis, and occasionally even further south on the west of Scotland. Some of the long-distance migrations are illustrated in Figure 13. These include the movement of a fish from the Moray Firth to the Inishtrahull grounds off the north of Ireland, a distance of approximately 375 miles by the most likely route, in 297 days, and of another from the Firth of Forth to the Butt of Lewis, a distance of roughly 330 miles, in 335 days.

When the direction followed by migrant lemon soles was studied along with a chart of the residual currents of the North Sea and its approaches (Tait, 1930) it was found that, apart from the few exceptions already referred to, the fish had been heading northwards into the dominant current. Further consideration of the records of the few fish which appeared to have followed a southerly direction within the North Sea, in relation to the subsidiary eddies of the Scottish east-coast current system, showed that their southward movement could be explained by the assumption that the fish had become involved in the northward flowing current on the western side of the eddies. Thus the contranatant explanation of migrating lemon soles could be maintained in spite of the apparent

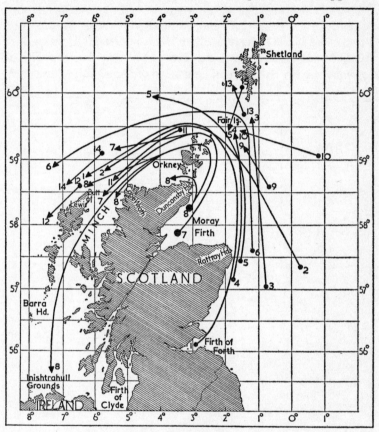

FIG. 13. Long distance migrations by Lemon Soles.

anomalies and ultimately these south-going migrants would reach a point, at the southern extremity of the eddies, where their movement would be forced by the changing direction of the current to assume a northerly direction. Such a course might bring them back to their position of liberation but, on the other hand, provided they encountered the main south-

going North Sea current, they also stood a chance of by-passing
their original position and of reaching even more northerly
grounds.

Seasonal Movements

Some of the records of shorter-distance and shorter-term
migrants, however, are more instructive (see Figure 14).
From these it has been possible to trace a seasonal movement of
fish towards certain grounds. The clearest evidence of this is
provided by the annual concentration of lemon soles on a small

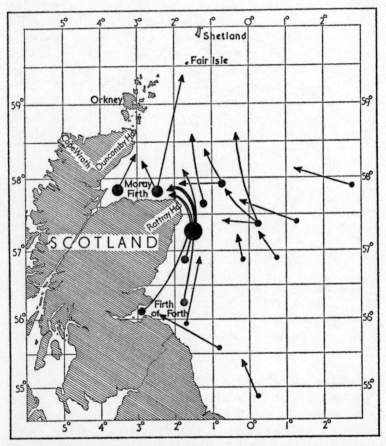

FIG. 14. Migrations by Lemon Soles within the North Sea: the small circles
represent single fish, the larger circles two or more fish.

bank to the west of Rosehearty, near the southern entrance to
the Moray Firth. This locality is the scene of a seine-net fishery
in the first quarter of every year. Marking experiments have
shown that this concentration follows the movement of lemon
soles from grounds to the south of Rattray Head. Slightly later
in the year similar concentrations occur in the northern half of
the Moray Firth, off the coast of Caithness, and in the vicinity
of Fair Isle. These concentrations would also appear to arise
from the migratory movement of lemon soles.

Speed of Migration

Some of the short-term migrants also provide useful information
in regard to the rate at which migration takes place. By
assuming that they travelled at a uniform rate by the shortest
route between the places of liberation and recapture it has been
calculated that the fish must have moved at a mean rate of over
two miles per day.

While the migratory movement is essentially seasonal in
character the impulse to move appears to be very irregular in
its incidence on the individual fish. As already indicated only a
proportion of the fish participate in the movement each year
and even among these the migratory urge is variable, both in
time and intensity.

Possible Cause of Migrations

The variable features of the migrations naturally give rise
to speculation as to why some lemon soles should move northwards away from grounds where the ecological conditions
ensure the most successful growth, to grounds where the food
supply and conditions for growth would appear to be less
favourable. However, the observation that the fish concerned
were all adult or approaching their first spawning, together
with the seasonal nature of the movement during the winter
and spring, clearly suggests that the migrations are linked
with the approaching spawning. This conclusion is also sup-
ported by numerous records of non-migrant fish which,
although not having travelled far enough to qualify for recognition as migrants, nevertheless, in many instances, revealed a
short northward movement.

It will be recalled that the eggs and larvae of lemon soles are carried southwards by the main North Sea current off the Scottish east coast. It has been concluded, therefore, that the northwards migrations of lemon soles represent the extreme aspects of a more general, but restricted, pre-spawning movement of adult fish arising from a natural urge to compensate for the southward drift of the eggs and larvae. Such a movement could well have evolved in response to the need to maintain the distribution of the species in its present ecological associations.

FISH TAGGING AS A MEANS OF MEASURING FISHING INTENSITY

Tagging experiments are also used as a means of ascertaining the rate at which stocks of fish are being exploited by commercial fisheries. By tagging and releasing a number (the larger the better) of fish in any area, and provided they are reasonably representative of the stock in every way, the rate at which the returns are received may be regarded as providing some indication of the rate of fishing. Some tagged fish of course die as a result of the tagging operations, some lose their tags, while others are undoubtedly killed by predators; almost certainly, too, a proportion is not returned through being overlooked by fishermen or merchants. Consequently only the recaptured fish can be utilized for estimation of the rate of fishing and, after allowing a suitable interval to elapse after the final returns are recorded, the experiment may be regarded as completed, because the stock represented by the tagged sample has been eliminated.

From the results of the Scottish tagging experiments in the North Sea and adjacent waters in the 1920s it was estimated that the adult lemon sole stock, as represented by the tagged fish, under the fishing conditions pertaining to those years, was almost completely fished out after four years. At that time this was regarded as extremely satisfactory since it was evident that many adult lemon soles survived to spawn several times before being caught. Subsequently, however, the intensity of fishing increased in the 1930s, so that it seems fairly certain that the chances of lemon sole survival were by then considerably reduced.

Some indication of the increase in the rate of capture on grounds fished by Scottish trawlers between the two wars was also derived from tagging experiments on lemon soles at Faroe.

While the rate of recapture of the tagged fish in this region during the 1920s was approximately the same as in the North Sea, the intensity of fishing later increased to such an extent that, by the 1930s, few tagged adult lemon soles were found to survive for longer than two years. This represents a remarkably high rate of fishing which is largely confirmed by the increase in the fishing effort by British trawlers at Faroe in the late 1920s and by the trebling of the Scottish catch and the doubling of the English catch of lemon soles on these grounds in the three years from 1929 to 1931. It is evident, moreover, that the stocks could not stand up to this strain for long from the equally sudden, although not so marked, decline in the Scottish and English landings over the next three years from 1932 to 1934.

Chapter VII

SOME ASPECTS OF LEMON SOLE FISHERIES

Some aspects of the fisheries for lemon soles acquire additional interest when considered in relation to scientific knowledge of the species. Its abundance on "hard" ground, which may be anything from rocks and boulders to gravel, and on the edge of banks, reflects the nature of its ecological relationships and indicates its rather specialized feeding habits.

THEIR SEASONAL NATURE
North Sea

The seasonal characteristics of lemon sole fisheries revealed by tagging experiments is still further emphasized by a study of commercial landings from a wider area throughout the year. Table VII gives the quantities of lemon soles landed from the entire North Sea by British trawlers, together with the average catch per 100 hours' fishing in each month from 1929 to 1938. It will be observed that landings are at their lowest ebb from December to March when the catch per 100 hours' fishing averages only about 1 cwt. This period of the year also coincides with the time when lemon sole feeding is least intensive. As we have seen, it is also the time when the adult fish perform their pre-spawning migrations. It is interesting to note, however, that the small but profitable fishery for lemon soles at the southern entrance to the Moray Firth occurs during this period of fasting and migration. This little fishery, which is by seine-net, does not fall within the main seasonal fishery for the North Sea.

Beginning in April the overall catch from the North Sea rises rapidly throughout May to reach a maximum which extends throughout June, July and August. Although there is some evidence of a decline in September, catches frequently continue at a high level into October, after which they fall off quickly. Obviously, therefore, the main lemon sole fishery in the North Sea lasts from May to October and thus coincides with both

TABLE VII

Monthly Landings of Lemon Soles and Catches per 100 hours' Fishing in cwt by British Trawlers from the North Sea, 1929–1938.

Month	1929	1930	1931	1932	1933	1934	1935	1936	1937	1938
January	2400 / 0·9	2657 / 1	2309 / 0·9	2753 / 1	2496 / 1	2477 / 1	3164 / 1	2471 / 1	1205 / 0·7	2351 / 1
February	1490 / 0·7	2858 / 1	1846 / 1	3164 / 2	2197 / 1	2806 / 2	3744 / 2	1879 / 0·9	2849 / 2	2629 / 2
March	1846 / 0·8	3411 / 1	1985 / 1	2492 / 1	2918 / 1	2995 / 2	4091 / 2	1694 / 0·8	2643 / 2	3438 / 2
April	2510 / 1	3788 / 2	2565 / 1	2514 / 2	3237 / 2	2713 / 1	3761 / 2	2014 / 1	4450 / 2	3741 / 2
May	4533 / 2	5814 / 3	4486 / 3	4623 / 3	5357 / 3	5649 / 3	7248 / 3	3838 / 2	5391 / 3	4604 / 3
June	5397 / 3	6126 / 3	4632 / 3	5480 / 3	6721 / 4	7218 / 3	7408 / 4	4876 / 3	6305 / 3	5905 / 4
July	8349 / 4	6129 / 3	5852 / 3	6417 / 4	6499 / 3	7098 / 3	7656 / 4	6078 / 3	6955 / 4	6743 / 4
August	7820 / 3	6099 / 3	5690 / 3	6791 / 3	6770 / 3	7455 / 3	8180 / 3	8083 / 3	6737 / 4	7634 / 4
September	7363 / 3	4969 / 2	6055 / 3	6526 / 3	6978 / 3	7187 / 3	6648 / 3	7114 / 4	6958 / 3	7000 / 4
October	7899 / 3	5519 / 2	6419 / 3	6008 / 3	6190 / 3	6646 / 3	5455 / 2	7889 / 3	6767 / 3	5733 / 3
November	4807 / 2	3658 / 2	3842 / 2	4500 / 2	4649 / 2	4878 / 2	3351 / 2	5765 / 3	4601 / 2	4183 / 2
December	2509 / 1	3826 / 2	3656 / 2	3518 / 2	3000 / 1	2804 / 2	2772 / 1	3902 / 2	3421 / 2	2681 / 2
Year	56,923 / 2	54,854 / 2	49,337 / 2	54,786 / 2	57,012 / 2	59,926 / 2	63,478 / 2	55,603 / 2	58,282 / 3	56,642 / 3

F*

the spawning season and the main feeding season for this fish. The fishery would seem to depend, therefore, on a successful exploitation of spawning and feeding concentrations. Although variable from year to year the catch per unit of fishing time at the height of the season may be six times as great as it is at midwinter.

Faroe

Average monthly landings of lemon soles by Scottish trawlers from Faroe over part of the same period have been condensed in Table VIII. The seasonal character of the lemon sole fishery in this region is again evident but with some interesting differences. At Faroe the "off-season" for lemons extends from October to February. An improvement in the catch in March is continued throughout April and May after which the catch rises rapidly to the summer maximum in June, July and August.

TABLE VIII

Average Monthly Catches of Lemon Soles by Scottish Trawlers from Faroe and Average Quantity taken per Unit of Fishing Time, 1933–1938

Month	Average catch of lemon soles in cwt	Average catch per 100 hrs' fishing in cwt
January	130	4·7
February	225	7·9
March	474	10·9
April	735	14·0
May	1002	22·4
June	1791	19·3
July	1823	17·7
August	1179	16·7
September	623	13·0
October	271	7·6
November	177	5·5
December	141	4·5

This is followed by a marked decline in September and October. The catch per unit of fishing time follows a somewhat similar course throughout the year, except for a sudden increase to a maximum in May, a feature which may possibly be linked in some way with the rather curious change in the general trawl fishery at Faroe from "dark" fishing in May to a "daylight and dark" fishing from June onwards to the end of the year.

OVER-FISHING

The greatest problem facing fisheries scientists in the last thirty years has undoubtedly been over-fishing of the stocks of the commercial food fishes. The possibility that stocks could be depleted had indeed occurred to some far-seeing individuals shortly after the turn of the century, but such warnings as were given were generally disregarded. The development of fishing power and the improvements in the efficiency of fishing gear which followed the first war led inevitably to a reduction of the stocks of fish in the North Sea and other home waters. For the first time there was a general realization that some fishing grounds were becoming less productive, and fisheries scientists were able to show that this was because the quantity of fish being removed annually from these grounds was greater than could be replaced by the natural functions of reproduction and growth—in other words that the stocks were being over-fished. Evidence of this undesirable state of affairs became available in the dwindling catches, in spite of increased effort, and in the declining quantity taken per unit of fishing time throughout most of the 1930s. The need for conservation measures became apparent and regulations were first put into effect by the United Kingdom in 1933. These were concerned with the enforcement of regulation sizes of mesh in the nets and minimum marketable sizes for certain important food species. In 1934, other species were added to the list, including the lemon sole, for which a minimum landing size of 9 inches (23 cm) was laid down. This was increased to 10 inches in 1948.

Following a recommendation by the International Council for the Exploration of the Sea in 1934 all the member countries of the Council resolved in 1937 to introduce similar regulations, but unfortunately the outbreak of war in 1939 put an end to further discussion and action.

Although talks on fish conservation were resumed after the war under the International Fisheries Convention (1946), positive action on an international basis was further delayed by the failure of the governments of some of the constituent countries to ratify the agreement until 1953. The regulations (including a minimum landing size of 25 cm for lemon soles) were at last introduced in 1956, but by this time it was apparent that differences in the traditional fisheries from one country to another were a very real obstacle to effective enforcement of the regulations. Moreover, the emergence and rapid development of new fisheries—the so-called industrial fisheries—in the years following the second war created further difficulties in the way of international co-operation. In 1959 the Convention of 1946 was replaced by the new and more flexible Convention for the North-East Atlantic Fisheries, which has now been ratified by the governments of the countries concerned.

In addition to being characterized by a decline in the total yearly catch and in the catch per unit of fishing effort, over-fishing is also identified by a marked diminution in the average size of the fish being caught. This is a direct result of the depletion of the stocks of older fish and the necessity for fishermen to rely more and more on young and often immature fish.

Although over-fishing is generally regarded as applying to all the fish on the affected grounds, the effects are most obvious in those species which provide the bulk of the catch. In the north-western North Sea these are haddock, cod and whiting. Of these the haddock (see Figure 2) is by far the most important species in Scottish fisheries and because of this, over-fishing in Scotland, to some extent, has come to be regarded as synonymous with over-fishing of haddock. In some measure, too, the effects of over-fishing on this species are linked with the marked fluctuations in its annual brood strengths.

While the fishing effort by Scottish fishermen is mainly directed towards the capture of the three most numerous species named above, the high prices obtained for flatfishes have often encouraged certain skippers to fish specifically for lemon soles, plaice, halibut or turbot. These four species of flatfish are of course rarely caught together on the same grounds, and the capture of each by any special effort is generally both local and seasonal.

The Effect of Intensive Fishing on Lemon Sole Stocks

It is interesting, therefore, to study the effect of fishing on the lemon sole stocks. For this purpose it is convenient to examine Table VII which gives the monthly landings in the United Kingdom from the North Sea by British trawlers, together with the catch per 100 hours' fishing for the period 1929 to 1938. These years are of particular interest because they are generally regarded as a time when over-fishing attained serious proportions in the North Sea. Table VII shows that after reaching a peak in 1935 landings fell slightly but continued at a level comparable with the average for the ten years. Turning to the catch per 100 hours' fishing, this is shown to vary from 1 to 4 cwt, depending on the season, in each of the ten years. In neither the total catch nor in the catch per 100 hours' fishing is there any evidence of over-fishing of the lemon sole stocks from 1929 to 1938. Indeed, Table VII, showing that an average catch of 4 cwt per unit of fishing time was obtained in only one month in 1929, compared with four months in 1938, would even suggest that better fishing was being obtained for lemon soles, at least at the height of the season, while the grounds were over-fished.

However, it is also necessary to consider the size-composition of the catch and for this purpose landings of lemon soles by Aberdeen trawlers from 1930 to 1938 are given in Table IX. This shows the number of trips made in each year to Scottish east-coast grounds, the total number of hours spent fishing, the average number of fishing hours per trip and the quantity of lemon soles in each of three market categories, with the appropriate catch per 100 hours' fishing. Although the total number of trips varied quite considerably from year to year, no consistent trend was observed over the nine years. On the other hand, the total number of hours spent fishing rose quite appreciably from less than 200,000 in the first three years to well over that figure in the latter half of the period. Moreover, the number of hours spent fishing per trip also rose steadily from less than thirty at the beginning of the period to thirty-five at its termination.

The size-composition of the lemon soles also reveals some interesting changes during the nine-year period. In 1930 nearly

half of the fish were in the "large" market category (range
35 to 45 cm: mean size 39·0 cm) while the quantities in the
"medium" (range 30–40 cm: mean size 34·2 cm) and "small"
(range 25–35 cm: mean size 29·5 cm) categories were about

TABLE IX

Fishing Effort and Catch of Lemon Soles by Aberdeen Trawlers
on Scottish East Coast Grounds, 1930–1938

Year	Number of trips	Total no. of hrs' fishing and average no. per trip	Total Catch of Lemon Soles and average weight per 100 hrs' fishing in cwt			
			Large	Medium	Small	Total
1930	6584	191659 29·1	10668 5·6	5439 2·8	5855 3·1	21962 11·5
1931	6266	184038 29·4	7610 4·1	5177 2·8	5532 3·0	18319 9·9
1932	5490	168995 30·8	7185 4·2	5429 3·2	6360 3·8	18974 11·2
1933	7025	214693 30·6	8116 3·8	6005 2·8	8648 4·0	22769 10·6
1934	6672	208889 31·3	6060 2·9	4953 2·4	11687 5·6	22700 10·9
1935	7749	257061 33·2	6071 2·4	6732 2·6	13979 5·4	26782 10·4
1936	7069	235321 33·3	5861 2·5	5348 2·3	13838 5·9	25047 10·7
1937	7571	264539 34·9	5410 2·0	4913 1·9	18256 6·9	28579 10·8
1938	6918	244888 35·4	5019 2·0	5534 2·3	16754 6·9	27307 11·2
1930–38	61344 6816	1970083 32·1	62000 3·1	49530 2·5	100909 5·1	212439 10·8

equal. From 1930 onwards, however, the quantity of large fish gradually declined until in 1938 less than one-fifth of the catch was of this size. Concurrently the quantity of medium-sized lemon soles also declined, although only slightly, while, in sharp contrast, the catch of small fish rose significantly from 3 cwt in 1930 and 1931 to nearly 7 cwt in 1937 and 1938. It is clear that although the same quantity of lemon soles was being caught per unit of fishing time in 1938 as in 1930, this was only being achieved by the landing of greater quantities of small fish. Research has shown that this preponderance of small fish in 1937 to 1938 was not the outcome of any natural phenomenon but was the result of the fishing out of the older or larger fish and the necessity for fishermen to rely on a keener selection of smaller fish to make up their catch.

In conclusion the position in regard to lemon soles in the North Sea during the period of over-exploitation of fish stocks prior to the second Great War may be summed up as follows. Although the total yearly catch and the catch of all sizes per unit of fishing time show no evidence of over-fishing, the growing effort required, in the form of more hours spent fishing per trip, and the greater dependence on small fish in obtaining a comparable catch clearly indicate that lemon sole stocks, if not over-fished, were at least being subjected to considerable strain. Similar conditions were found to prevail on Faroese grounds during the same period.

As a result of the reduced fishing effort during the second war the size-composition of lemon soles, both in the North Sea and at Faroe, like all other species, recovered to such an extent that the catch in the immediate post-war years again included a high proportion of large fish. At Faroe, for example, the lemon sole catch by Aberdeen trawlers in 1945 consisted of 50% large fish and 16% small, whereas in 1938 the corresponding figures were 14% large and 66% small. From 1945 onwards, however, each year saw a further decline in the quantity of large fish and a renewed dependence on small fish. Although no recent research has been carried out on the lemon sole it seems likely that the size-composition of the stocks in both regions is once more comparable with that of the late 1930s.

The evidence acquired from the accumulation of fish stocks following the reduced fishing effort of the second war years reveals the natural ability of stocks of fish of all kinds to recover when given the opportunity of doing so. It also indicates the possibility, provided international agreement were achieved, of regulating fishing effort and so obtaining a steady optimum catch from year to year. Unfortunately this desirable situation is still very far from being realized.

POSSIBLE REASONS FOR THE RESISTANCE OF LEMON SOLE STOCKS TO OVER-FISHING

It is interesting to consider why the lemon sole presents no clear evidence of over-fishing while other more plentiful species are obviously being over-exploited under these conditions. This may be because of the fact that on most grounds, and for the greater part of the year, the lemon sole is not the object of any special fishery and is caught only incidentally while fishermen are concentrating on the capture of the more numerous gadoids. A more likely explanation, however, seems to lie in some features of the fish's life. In the first place the spawning season, as we have seen, extends over the greater part of the year, March to November. This feature in itself tends to reduce natural fluctuations in brood strengths to a minimum and thus helps to ensure a fairly uniform annual recruitment to the stocks. The prolonged spawning season also results in a considerable spread in the size-composition of the fish in each brood, for obviously fish hatched at the beginning of the season start off with a considerable advantage over those derived from a late spawning. Finally, the relatively slow rate of growth of the species and local differences in the growth rate both help to maintain a stock of fish of all sizes and including a relatively large number of different broods. Each of these factors would seem to contribute to the maintenance of a relatively stable stock capable of withstanding the fishing effort from year to year. Furthermore, it seems not unlikely that such fluctuations in the annual catch of lemon soles, as have been recorded, arise more from variations in the fishing effort than from natural fluctuations in the stock.

Chapter VIII

VARIOUS BIOLOGICAL FEATURES

PARASITES AND DISEASES

Larvae of Lernaeocera obtusa

Kabata (1958) has shown that the lemon sole serves as an intermediate host for a parasitic copepod *Lernaeocera obtusa* which infests the gills of haddock. The larvae of the parasite attach themselves to the gills of the lemon sole soon after hatching from the eggs in the water. Infestation of the lemon sole increases throughout March and April to reach a maximum in May. By this time the earlier larvae have developed, and from May to June, after attaining the adult state, they begin to leave their intermediate host in search of their final or definitive host, the haddock. A reinfestation by larvae of the earliest stage occurs in July, after which the larvae develop and gradually decrease in numbers as the adult parasites depart to seek their final host. A marked increase in the infestation of haddock by the adult parasites has been observed following their departure from their first or intermediate host. It has been estimated that in some localities 96% of the lemon soles may be infested by the larvae of *Lernaeocera obtusa* but there is no evidence that this infestation has any harmful effect on the host.

Worm Parasites

Many commercially valuable fish are heavily infested with worm parasites on certain grounds. Infestation may be by larval forms encysted in one or another of the different organs or, more rarely, in the muscles or flesh. Some species may also carry heavy loads of parasitic worms, larval and adult, in their alimentary canal, but this condition presents no problem from the commercial viewpoint since the parasites are disposed of in the gutting of the fish. Although nematode and trematode worms have occasionally been found in the stomach or intestine, and, on a few rare occasions, plerocercoid larvae of a cestode have been identified in the flesh, the lemon sole would appear to be comparatively free from worm infestation.

Fish Diseases

It is known that fish occasionally suffer from a piscine form of some of the diseases which afflict the higher animals although it is extremely doubtful if such diseases are transmissible to man. Examples of diseased fish, however, rarely come to the notice of marine scientists, partly it would seem because such specimens are particularly vulnerable under natural conditions and few survive predation in the sea long enough to allow them to be caught, and partly because fishermen instinctively discard anything repulsive and likely to spoil the appearance of their catch. This, to some extent, probably explains why so few diseased lemon soles have been recorded. Specimens with a skin infection have been observed from time to time and on one occasion, in August 1935, a catch of 56 cwt of lemon soles from off Fuglo Head in the Faroes included 7 stones of fish with open sores. These sores, which were about the size of a shilling or a florin, occurred on different parts of the fish from the head to the tail. Most of them were located on the underside and two or three were sometimes present on a single fish. Although their appearance at the time suggested some ulcerous condition, no satisfactory explanation was obtained, and indeed one can't be certain that the wounds were not initially caused by some predatory attack.

On rare occasions tumours or growths are encountered in fishes. These are, however, very unusual in flatfishes; so much so that in records maintained over a period of fifty years only two lemon soles exhibiting growth-like features have been received at the Marine Laboratory. In one of these an oval swelling, roughly 7·8 cm × 4·4 cm, extended from the base of the dorsal fin across the upper side of the fish halfway to the lateral line. For various reasons these specimens were not examined by an expert so that no opinions can be expressed as to their nature or origin.

In referring to the occurrence of these abnormal features in fish it must be emphasized that by no means all the swellings or "growths" indicate a diseased condition. On many occasions they merely represent some structural abnormality, with no pathological significance, resulting from injury.

Undoubtedly, the knowledge that food fishes are susceptible to disease may cause a slight feeling of revulsion in some individuals, but it should be remembered that all food, whether of vegetable or animal origin, is liable to be similarly affected, and that it is to meet this possibility that Public Health Authorities have instituted rigid food inspection methods.

ABNORMALITIES

Fishermen in general are intensely interested in unusual specimens which come up in their nets. Evidence of this trait is provided by the numbers of rare fish presented every year to the Marine Laboratory at Aberdeen and no doubt to similar institutions elsewhere. Abnormal specimens, whether in the form of a hump-backed cod, a "golden" haddock, or occasionally that old fisherman's trick, a three-eyed flatfish, are also sent regularly in the expectation of receiving some explanatory note. Judging by the Aberdeen records structural and colour abnormalities would seem to be rather more numerous and varied in flatfishes than in roundfish. No doubt they may to some extent be explained by mutations in the structural changes which flatfishes go through during their metamorphosis from the larval state.

Abnormalities appear to be just as frequent among lemon soles as they are in other flatfishes. The following typical examples have been recorded at Aberdeen:—

Colour Deficiency

Colour in the skin of fishes is contained in numerous pigment cells or chromatophores. The granules of pigment in these cells may be red, orange, yellow or black and the visible colour of the individual fish depends on the state of expansion or contraction of the various chromatophores. The ability of fish to change colour and thus merge with their surroundings is facilitated by this mechanism. Occasionally one or more of the colours may be lacking from the skin of individual fish, thus restricting their range of colour variation and increasing the possibility of abnormalities.

A number of bright orange-red or dark-red lemon soles presented to the laboratory by fishermen have been found on microscopic examination of the scales to have little or no black pigment in their skins. One of these fish, curiously enough, had been feeding heavily on the fronds of *Polysiphonia* and other red algae. A dark green lemon sole, on the other hand, revealed the complete absence of red and orange pigment. This fish was also exceptional in that it exhibited dark patches on the body (but not on the fins) corresponding to the black spots which are so characteristic of the larval stages. Normally these dark patches disappear when metamorphosis is completed. Although one cannot be certain of the causes of colour deficiency a probable explanation is that it results from some physiological upset in the fish.

Ambicoloration

Normally, flatfishes are coloured only on their upper side while their underside remains white. Occasionally pigmentation extends to the underside, rarely over its entire surface, sometimes confined to the anterior or posterior half of the fish, but more frequently occurring in patches or large spots. This condition is known as ambicoloration.

One lemon sole has been recorded completely coloured on both sides except for the underside of the head which was white, while at least three others have been observed with varying amounts of colour on the underside.

This condition would seem to be in the nature of a throwback to an early symmetrical form with colour on both sides in the evolution of the lemon sole.

"Reversed" Lemon Soles

The term "reversed" has been applied to those flatfishes with eyes on the opposite side of the head from the usual specific feature. In the lemon sole the eyes normally are on the right side of the head. The records of the Marine Laboratory, which extend over a period of fifty years, contain four examples of "reversed" lemon soles, with their eyes on their left side. The first of these was landed at Wick in May 1933, the second at the same port in April 1939, the third at Leith in May 1939, and the fourth at Aberdeen in November 1956. These records indicate the extreme rarity of this condition, although others undoubtedly occur in nature but are overlooked by the fishermen. The most likely explanation of the reversed state would seem to be some upset to the mechanism of the metamorphosis.

Development of Additional Fins

Another abnormality which may also be associated with a derangement of the metamorphosis is the occurrence of fish

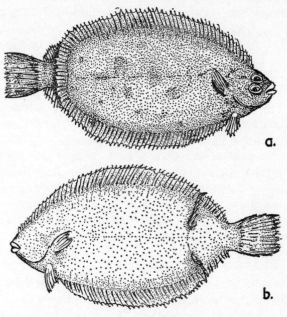

FIG. 15. Abnormal fin development in Lemon Soles.

with additional fins. Four lemon soles in this category have been presented to the laboratory from 1924 to 1963. In each the abnormality consisted of accessory fins branching off the dorsal and ventral fins in the posterior half of the body and extending across towards or over the lateral line. In three of the four specimens the fins were attached to the underside along their entire lengths. In one example (Figure 15b) the fins slanted forward from their point of attachment with the dorsal and ventral fins while the fin rays gradually became shorter so that near the lateral line they were merely rudimentary. In another specimen the accessory fins were on the upper side and branching off the dorsal and ventral fins near the caudal peduncle (Figure 15a). In this example it will be noted that the two branches coalesce over the lateral line and that the fin rays were of fairly uniform length throughout.

Skeletal Abnormalities

Examples of hump-back fish, the result of vertebral deformity, are not uncommon among cod and haddock. This condition is rarer in flatfishes, probably because it may be more difficult to detect, but at least one hump-backed lemon sole has been recorded. This specimen and other deformed lemon soles (short in relation to their breadth) have been found on dissection to have some of their vertebrae either fused or compressed like a concertina. Skeletal deformities of this nature may have been caused by injury or subjection to unusual conditions during the larval life of the fish.

Although various suggestions have been made as to the possible causes of these abnormalities little research has been carried out on this subject. Consequently one can't be certain and the possibility of other factors, for example heredity, also having some effect on the incidence of abnormal features cannot be disregarded.

THE OCCURRENCE OF MUTILATED FISH

In addition to the abnormalities already referred to lemon soles exhibiting other unusual structural features or evidence of injury suffered at some stage in their lives are obtained from commercial sources from time to time. Three of these, all healthy fish at capture, appeared to have had portions removed, two of them dorsally and one ventrally, possibly through being attacked by a predator (Figure 16). On each occasion the wound, if indeed the condition originated in this way, had healed perfectly. No suggestion can be offered as to when these mutilations were suffered but it is interesting to note that the alimentary tract of the fish with the portion missing on its ventral side was intact (Figure 16b). This seems to indicate that the abnormality had developed, whether as a result of injury or some other cause, during the larval state before the development of the gut had extended backwards to the position it occupies in the adolescent fish. Rather more puzzling, however, is the lemon sole with a perforation of its dorsal region (Figure 16c).

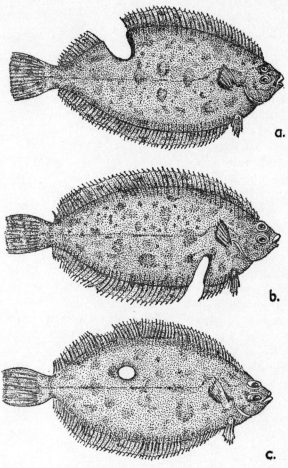

FIG. 16. Mutilated Lemon Soles.

On 28th October, 1963 a blind lemon sole was examined at the Marine Laboratory. One eye was missing and the eye socket completely overgrown by skin. The other eye had been almost completely destroyed except for the remains of various tissues. Again it is difficult to account for this mutilation but the fish may possibly have been attacked by a bird. For example, fish brought up in fishermen's nets occasionally escape at the surface of the water, where they are at the mercy of gulls, until they are able to submerge. The remarkable fact about this specimen is that it apparently had survived the injuries for some time.

PREDATORS

Information concerning predators on the lemon sole can only be confirmed by the identification of the remains of the fish in the stomach contents of other fish and marine animals. Investigation of the food of fishes at the Marine Laboratory, Aberdeen, has shown lemon soles to be eaten more frequently by cod than by any other fish but even so, the lemon sole, by comparison with other organisms, is not a common item in the cod's diet. The latter species is an omnivorous feeder and the larger cod feed predominantly on fish of all kinds. Preliminary observations in Scottish waters seem to suggest that the frequency with which cod eat the various species of fish depends to some extent on the numbers of each kind available. Consequently lemon soles are eaten far less frequently than the various gadoids and sand eels, for example. Halibut (Scott, 1901), turbot, long rough dabs (Smith, 1892 and Hørring, 1901), dogfish (*Squalus acanthias*), gurnard and sea trout (O'Donoghue & Boyd, 1934) have also been known to prey on the lemon sole. It seems a reasonable assumption, therefore, that any fish-eating species occupying the same ecological niche as the lemon sole is likely to be a possible predator. Naturally size is an important factor in predator-prey considerations and even the larval stages have their enemies among the smaller fish.

BIBLIOGRAPHY

Bowman, A. (1914). The distribution of plaice eggs in the northern North Sea. *Sci. Invest. Fish. Bd Scot.*, 1914 (2), 67.

— (1921). The distribution of plaice eggs in the northern North Sea–II. *Sci. Invest. Fish. Bd Scot.*, 1921 (1), 33.

— (1935). Spawning migrations of plaice and lemon soles. *VIIe Congr. int. Aquicult. Pêche*, 1931.

Bowman, A. and Rae, B. B. (1936). Lemon soles (*Pleuronectes microcephalus*). Marking experiments in Scottish waters during the period 1919–1931. *Sci. Invest. Fish. Bd Scot.*, 1935 (1), 42.

Clark, R. S. (1920). The pelagic young and early bottom stages of teleosteans. *J. mar. biol. Ass. U.K.*, n.s. 12 (2), 159–240.

Cunningham, J. T. (1890). Studies on the reproduction and development of teleostean fishes occurring in the neighbourhood of Plymouth. *J. mar. biol. Ass. U.K.*, n.s. 1, 10–54.

— (1891–92) The rate of growth of some sea fishes and their distribution at different ages. *J. mar. biol. Ass. U.K.*, n.s. 2, 95–118.

— (1893). The immature fish question. *J. mar. biol. Ass. U.K.*, n.s. 3, 54–77.

— (1893). Researches on the coloration of the skins of flatfishes. *J. mar. biol. Ass. U.K.*, n.s. 3, 111–118.

— (1896). The natural history of the marketable marine fishes of the British Islands. London: Macmillan, 375.

Dannevig, H. (1895). On hatching operations at Dunbar Marine hatchery. *Rep. Fish. Bd Scot.*, 14 (3), 150–157.

— (1897). Report on the operations at Dunbar Marine hatchery for the period July 1896 to December 1897 with some notes on rearing experiments with flatfishes. *Rep. Fish. Bd Scot.*, 16 (3), 219–224.

Day, F. (1880–84). The Fishes of Great Britain and Ireland. 2 vols. London: Williams & Norgate.

Ehrenbaum, E. (1909). Eier und Larven von Fischen des nordeschen Planktons. *Nord. Plankt.*, 1 (1–2), 413.

Fulton, T. W. (1889). The spawning and spawning places of marine food fishes. *Rep. Fish. Bd Scot.*, 8 (3), 257–269.

— (1890). The comparative fecundity of sea fish. *Rep. Fish. Bd Scot.*, 9 (3), 243–268.

— (1891). Observations on the reproduction, maturity and sexual relations of the food fishes. *Rep. Fish. Bd Scot.*, 10 (3), 232–244.

— (1892). An experimental investigation on the migrations and rate of growth of the food fishes. *Rep. Fish. Bd Scot.*, 11 (3), 176–196.

— (1901). Report on the trawling experiments of the "Garland", and on the fishery statistics relating thereto. *Rep. Fish. Bd Scot.*, 20 (3), 17–72.

— (1902). Investigations on the abundance, distribution and migrations of the food fishes. *Rep. Fish. Bd Scot.*, 21 (3), 15–108.

Fulton, G. W. (1905). On the distribution and seasonal abundance of flat-fishes (Pleuronectidae) in the North Sea. *Rep. North Sea Fish. Invest. Comm.*, North Area no. 1, 1902–03, 473–618.

FULLARTON, J. H. (1888). Report on bait experiments. *Rep. Fish. Bd Scot.*, **7**, 352–364.

HENKING, H. (1905). On the periodic occurrence of the principal food fishes in the North Sea and Skagerrak based on the returns of German fishing steamers. *Rapp. Cons. Explor. Mer*, **3** Append. F, 28.

HOLT, E. W. L. (1891). Survey of fishing grounds on the west coast [of Ireland]. Report on the scientific evidence on economic questions. Fishes. *Rep. R. Dublin Soc.*, 1890–91, 241–329.

— (1892). North Sea investigations. *J. mar. biol. Ass. U.K.*, n.s. **2**, 216–219.

— (1893). Survey of fishery grounds, West coast of Ireland, 1890–91: on the eggs and larval and post-larval stages of teleosteans. *Sci. Trans. R. Dublin Soc.*, ser. 2, **5** (2), 121.

— (1893). Notes and memoranda: *Pleuronectes microcephalus*, Donovan. *J. mar. biol. Ass. U.K.*, n.s. **3**, 121.

— (1895). An examination of the present state of the Grimsby trawl fishery, with especial reference to the destruction of immature fish. *J. mar. biol. Ass. U.K.*, n.s. **3**, 339.

HØRRING, R. (1901). Indberetning foretagne fiskeriundersøgelser ved Island og Faerøerne. *FiskBeretn., Kbh.*, 1900–01, 204.

KABATA, Z. (1958). *Lernaeocera obtusa* n.sp. Its biology and its effect on the haddock. *Mar. Res. Scot.*, 1958 (3), 26.

KYLE, H. M. (1897). The post-larval stages of the plaice, dab, flounder, long rough dab and lemon sole. *Rep. Fish. Bd Scot.*, **16**, 225–247.

— (1899). The classification of the flatfishes (Heterosomata). *Rep. Fish. Bd Scot.*, **18**, 335.

LEBOUR, M. V. (1918). The food of post-larval fish. *J. mar. biol. Ass. U.K.*, **11** (4), 433–469.

McINTOSH, W. C. (1890). Further observations on the life histories and development of the food and other fishes. *Rep. Fish. Bd Scot.*, **9**, 317–342.

McINTOSH, W. C. and MASTERMAN, A. T. (1897). The life-histories of the British marine food-fishes. Cambridge Univ. Press, 516.

MAIER, H. M. (1906). Beiträge zur Altersbestimmung der Fische. *Wiss. Meeresuntersuch.*, Abt. Kiel, **8**, 57–115.

MASTERMAN, A. T. (1909). Report on the later stages of the Pleuronectidae. *Rapp. Cons. Explor. Mer*, **12** (4), 82.

NORMAN, J. R. (1934). A systematic monograph of the flatfishes (Heterosomata). 1. Psettodidae, Bothidae, Pleuronectidae. London. Brit. Mis. (*Nat. Hist.*), 459

O'DONOGHUE, C. H. and BOYD, E. M. (1934). A third investigation of the food of the sea trout (*Salmo trutta*), with a note on the food of the perch (*Perca fluviatilis*). *Salm. Fish., Fish. Bd Scot.*, 1934 (2), 21.

PAWSEY, E. S. and DAVIS, F. M. (1924). Report on exploratory voyages to Lousy Bank and adjacent areas. *Fish. Invest., Lond.*, ser. 2, **7** (2), 22.

PETERSEN, C. G. J. (1904). On the larval and post-larval stages of the long rough dab and the genus *Pleuronectes. Medd. Komm. Havundersøg., Kbh. ser. Fisk.*, **1** (1), 12.

RAE, B. B. (1939). Age and growth of lemon soles in Scottish waters. *Sci. Invest. Fish. Bd Scot.*, 1939 (1), 39.

RAE, B. B. (1939). Marking experiments on lemon soles at Faroe 1923–1936, with a note on Icelandic marking 1925. *J. Cons. int. Explor. Mer*, **14** (1), 35–47.

— (1939). Lemon soles at Faroe, 1923–1938. *Rapp. Cons. Explor. Mer*, **109** (2), 15–28.

— (1939). The food of lemon soles in Faroese waters. *Rapp. Cons. Explor. Mer*, **109** (3), 29–36.

— (1939). Factors in the growth of lemon soles. *Sci. Invest. Fish. Bd Scot.*, 1939 (3), 18.

— (1947). Review of the Scottish lemon sole fishery at Faroe with special reference to the years 1933 to 1938. *J. Cons. int. Explor. Mer*, **15** (1), 61–68.

— (1948). Lemon soles at Iceland, 1924–1939, with special reference to Faxa Bay. *J. Cons. int. Explor. Mer*, **15** (3), 295–317.

— (1948). Lemon sole in Faxa Bay. *Rapp. Cons. Explor. Mer*, **120** (10), 46–51.

— (1951). A comparison of the pre-war and post-war stocks of lemon soles at Faroe. *J. Cons. int. Explor. Mer*, **17** (3), 242–260.

— (1953). The occurrence of lemon sole larvae in the Scottish plankton collections of 1929, 1930 and 1931. *Mar. Res. Scot.*, 1953 (1), 36.

— (1956). The food and feeding habits of the lemon sole. *Mar. Res. Scot.*, 1956 (3), 32.

— (1959). Halibut—observations on its size at first maturity, sex ratio and length-weight relationship. *Mar. Res. Scot.*, 1959 (4), 19.

RAITT, D. S. (1936). The haddock stocks of the north-east Atlantic, 1916–1935. *Sci. Invest. Fish. Bd Scot.*, 1936 (1), 32.

RITCHIE, A. (1960). The Scottish seine-net fishery, 1921–1957. *Mar. Res. Scot.*, 1960 (3), 68

SCOTT, T. (1901). Observations on the food of fishes. *Rep. Fish. Bd Scot.*, **20** (3), 486–541.

SMITH, W. R. (1889). On the food of fishes. *Rep. Fish. Bd Scot.*, 7 (3), 222–258.

— (1890). On the food of fishes. *Rep. Fish. Bd Scot.*, 8 (3), 230–256.

— (1891). On the food of fishes. *Rep. Fish. Bd Scot.*, 9 (3), 222–242.

— (1892). On the food of fishes. *Rep. Fish. Bd Scot.*, 10 (3), 231.

SMITT, F. A. (1893). A history of Scandinavian fishes. 3 vols. in 2, Stockholm.

STEVEN, G. A. (1930). Bottom fauna and the food of fishes. *J. mar. biol. Ass. U.K.*, **16** (3), 677–700.

STORROW, B. (1916). Notes on the age and growth of fish. *Rep. Dove Mar. Lab.*, n.s. **5**, 38–53.

STRUBBERG, A. C. (1918). Marking experiments with plaice and lemon soles at the Faroes in 1910–1912. *Medd. Komm. Havundersøg., ser Fisk.*, **5** (6), 64.

SUND, O. (1938). Die Norwegische Seefischerei *Handb. Seefisch. Nordeurop.*, **8** (1a), 181.

TAIT, J. B. (1930). The surface water drift in the northern and middle areas of the North Sea and in the Faroe-Shetland Channel. Pt. 1. *Sci. Invest. Fish. Bd Scot.*, 1930 (2), 82.

— (1937). The surface water drift in the northern and middle areas of the North Sea and in the Faroe-Shetland Channel. Pt. 2, sect. 3. *Sci. Invest. Fish. Bd Scot.*, 1937 (1), 60.

TÅNING, A. V. (1939). Fiske forsøg epter rødtunger ved Faerøerne i 1939. *Fisk Beretn.*, *Kbh.*, 1939, 107–108.

— (1943). Fiskeri-og Havundersøgelser ved Faerøerne. *Skr. Komm. Havunders.*, *Kbh.*, No. 12, 127.

THOMPSON, H. (1928). The haddock of the north-western North Sea. *Sci. Invest. Fish. Bd Scot.*, 1927 (3), 20.

TODD, R. A. (1905). Report on the food of fishes collected during 1903. *Rep. North Sea Fish. Invest. Comm.*, South Area no. 1, 227–287.

— (1907). Second report on the food of fishes (North Sea, 1904–05). *Rep. North Sea Fish. Invest. Comm.*, South Area no. 2 (1), 49–163.

WALLACE, W. (1923). Report on experimental hauls with small trawls in certain inshore waters off the east coast of England. *Fish. Invest., Lond.*, ser. 2, **5** (5), 30.

WILLIAMSON, H. C. (1892). On the rate of growth of certain marine food-fishes. *Rep. Fish. Bd Scot.*, **11** (3), 265–282.

BULLETIN STATISTIQUE DES PÊCHES MARITIMES, COPENHAGUE 1951–60.

SEA FISHERIES STATISTICAL TABLES FOR ENGLAND AND WALES 1903–1962. (Published up to 1918 in Annual Report on Sea Fisheries, Board of Agriculture and Fisheries.)

SCOTTISH SEA FISHERIES STATISTICAL TABLES 1882–1962. (Published up to 1917 in Annual Report of the Fishery Board for Scotland.)

INDEX

The term "lemon sole" is implied and not printed in most of the entries in this index.

Page references to illustrations are given in italics